Dr. Melanie Beingessner

Library and Archives Canada Cataloguing in Publication

Beingessner, Melanie, 1967-, author
The calm baby cookbook / Dr. Melanie Beingessner. – 2nd revised edition.

Issued in print and electronic formats.
ISBN 978-0-9739455-4-6 (softcover).–ISBN 978-0-9739455-3-9 (EPUB).–
ISBN 978-0-9739455-2-2 (Kindle)

1. Breastfeeding. 2. Mothers–Nutrition. 3. Cooking. 4. Cookbooks.
I. Title.

RJ216.B36 2017   641.5'630852   C2017-902427-2   C2017-902428-0

Heartlights Publishing
505 Centre Avenue E
Airdrie, AB Canada T4B 1P9
www.heartlightspublishing.com

Table of Contents

Book Reviews

"I came to Dr. Melanie with concerns about my daughter's gas pains and reflux. Blake would cry throughout the day and the night as well. I tried colic medicines, the bicycle pumps with her legs, different ways of positioning her and warm baths. Nothing worked. I had heard that chiropractic adjustments could help, so I thought that I'd give it a try. Dr. Melanie noticed tension in her spine, her stomach and suggested that I should change my diet. It was amazing!

Within a week, Blake was a calmer and happier baby, and of course I was a happy mama as well. Doing an elimination diet made a noticeable difference almost immediately. Our day to day routine is much easier and less stressful on my husband and myself.

The Calm Baby Cookbook has wonderful recipes that are a great help."

Beth P. – new mom

When Conner was about 2 months old he started to seem uncomfortable and extremely gassy which was affecting his sleep and he was no longer the happy baby we were used to. We had been going to the chiropractor since Conner was about 6 weeks old as he was slightly out of alignment from a rushed delivery. When I mentioned to Dr. Melanie Conner's new change in behaviour she suggested removing certain foods from my diet to see if it made a difference for Conner since he is breastfed.

A few weeks after removing dairy from my diet, he was a new baby. He was less gassy and was sleeping much better at night. He also returned to the happy baby we were used to. Every month I try dairy in hopes that he has grown out of this sensitivity, but like clockwork, 24 hours later he is extremely gassy and uncomfortable again.

Allison B. – Mother of 2

As a father, I wish I had this book a long time ago. I still recall the frustration and sadness my wife and I felt as our colicky first-born suffered night after night. The feeling of failure was quite overwhelming. Dr. Melanie has done a masterful job of taking a super-stressful subject and simplifying it for all parents. If even one parent can avoid the confusion and pain that so many go through with their newborns, Dr. Melanie has made a huge contribution.

As a practicing chiropractor, I can't wait to get this book into the hands of every one of my patients. I am constantly asked questions regarding nutrition for infants, and to have this resource in my bag of tricks will be invaluable. Thank you, Dr. Melanie for your dedication and for sharing your brilliance.

Dr. Rick Markson – Chiropractor, Team Leader of ChiroDestiny

Dr. Melanie has created the short and sweet guide to helping you figure out how to help your baby become a calm one. Having known and worked with Dr. Melanie for over a decade, I have come to rely on her excellent care of moms and babies in her chiropractic practice. I recommend that moms read and implement a Calm Baby approach to save themselves and their little ones hours of unnecessary upset. Take back the night!

Dr. Allissa Gaul – Naturopath and Creator of Helpingdrmom.com

The miracle of a newborn baby promises joy to the new parents. After months of anticipation the tiny bundle has finally arrived. Now there is nothing to do but feed the little one, change the odd diaper and enjoy every new achievement. First the gurgles and smiles, then looking forward to the next milestone. What could be more rewarding? But sometimes the little one is fussy and difficult to settle. What to do? What to do? Dr. Melanie's book offers some very practical advice for helping parents cope. With her years of experience both as a chiropractor and mother of three children she has many ideas of how to solve the problem.

Her first "Calm Baby Cookbook" included recipes of foods that would avoid a baby with an upset tummy. This second book explains how other problems may cause a baby to be irritable for prolonged periods of time. Dr. Melanie discusses these issues, whether caused by muscle strain, joint problems, digestive issues, allergies or food sensitivities. This book will be a great help for the day to day "what should I try next" question. When parents have been awake with a crying baby for several hours it is always good to have some new ideas close at hand. This book will be a great addition to the "New Baby" library.

Elaine Montgomery - Retired Registered Nurse, and Doula

What a great resource for new mothers! Dr. Melanie does a great job of giving insightful and detailed information in this book. I wish I had The Calm Baby Cookbook when my children were born.

Dr. Rachel Northern - Chiropractor,
and Author of A Journey to Vibrant Health

The Calm Baby Cookbook is an excellent resource for all new moms. Simple suggestions with good explanations. This book belongs on every bookshelf next to What to Expect When Your Expecting. I know it will be a frequent resource in my office, and for my patients.

Dr. Tiffany Attilio - Registered Nurse, Chiropractor,
Author of Creating Awesome! Radiant Health as a Spiritual Practice

Your Free Gift

As a way of saying thank you for your purchase, I'd like to offer you a free Infant Massage Kit that's exclusive to my book and blog readers.

Infant massage offers so many benefits to both the baby and the person giving the massage. It is a delightful way to use the power of touch to improve your baby's:

- intelligence
- digestion
- sleep
- bonding time with you!

Many new mothers want to learn infant massage, but have difficulty finding a place, or the time to learn. Timing is everything. To make life easier for the new moms in my clinic, I self-produced two infant massage videos that I'd like to share with you. The infant massage kit contains –

- An introductory video that tells you all that you need to know before you get started
- A video that shows the infant massage strokes. You can place your computer screen next to your baby and follow along
- A pdf summary of what you need to know about infant massage
- A pdf chart that outlines the infant massage strokes

You can download this free infant massage kit at

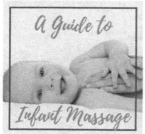

https://www.awesomemomtips.com/infant-massage-kit

www.awesomemomtips.com

To Cody, Kayla and Amanda
I love you to the moon and back.
And to Bruce, the love of my life,
You always make everything possible.

Introduction

More than 10 years ago, my friend Judith and I created a prenatal class to help pregnant couples transition to family life. Our prenatal class was called Becoming Parents and it was designed to teach about labor and birth, and to help parents realize that birth was not the finish line. *There is no finish line.* A woman gives birth and then she picks herself up and carries on to learn to breastfeed and care for her baby. We felt that if women and their partners were better prepared for the reality of life with a newborn, they had a much easier chance to shift into family life.

Judith was the childbirth educator; she taught the labor and birth section. I am a chiropractor, a breastfeeding counselor, and a mother of three. With my personal experience, I taught about the 24-hour day of parenting, how your relationships change after your baby is born, sex after baby, the mechanics of breastfeeding, and what to do if your baby is fussy.

Our prenatal class was going quite well, and we were improving it as we went along. One day, Judith said to me, "You know that breastfeeding section about fussy babies? You should write a book about that. All breastfeeding moms need to know this information."

That was the beginning of the book that you are now holding.

Many babies transition to this world easily. Their breastfeeding mom could eat salsa and jalapeño nachos and they remain calm and sleep well. These babies have an easier start to life.

Some babies don't have it that easy. They fuss and cry in the late evening and into the night, and new parents simply don't know what to do to help their baby feel better. Everyone is exhausted at the end of the day and many new parents think to themselves, "I'm not sure I can do this," or even worse, "There's something wrong with me."

If you have purchased this book, and your baby is one of the fussy ones, or if you are preparing in advance in case your baby will be fussy, I hope that you find these concepts helpful. They certainly made my life better. I have shared these ideas with my patients over the past 20 years and most of them have benefited from eliminating specific foods from their diets during the early days of breastfeeding.

Breastmilk is healthier than formula – it contains the perfect proportion of nutrients, fats, and antibodies to improve brain and nerve function and provide immunity from viruses and bacterial infections. The longer you breastfeed, the more positively you affect your baby's health – and I applaud you for not giving up. Many women do, when they're at their wit's end and the baby won't calm down. But sometimes all it takes is a tweak or two for breastfeeding to become easier, and I truly hope that this book will provide the missing link to what you need to help your baby settle at home.

Thank you for persevering on your breastfeeding journey, and all my best to you and your family.

Dr. Melanie Beingessner

About the Author

Dr. Melanie Beingessner is a pregnancy and pediatric-focused chiropractor with more than 20 years of clinical experience treating pregnant and new moms, infants, and children. She is the owner of Blessingways Family Wellness, a multidisciplinary clinic that focuses on family health and wellness.

Dr. Melanie has taken 180 hours of post graduate classes towards diplomate status from the International Chiropractic Pediatric Association. She is a breastfeeding counselor and a certified infant massage instructor with the International Association of Infant Massage.

Dr. Melanie is also the mother of three fabulous kids – Cody, Kayla, and Amanda. She lives in Calgary, Alberta, Canada with her husband, Bruce, their kids, and their two cats. For fun, Dr. Melanie practices tai chi and swims, and she loves to quilt.

Dr. Melanie's blog on mothering is full of information for moms of babies, children, and teens. Please check it out at www.awesomemomtips.com.

Congratulations, it's a boy!

When referring to babies in general, it is very awkward to continually refer to "he or she" or "him or her." To make it simpler for all of us, the baby of our book will be a boy. Then, moms will be "she" or "her," the baby can be "he" or "him," and we will all know who I'm talking about.

Calmer Babies Bond More Easily with Their Families

A fussy, crying, inconsolable baby is very stressful for new parents. You do your best to respond to your baby's needs, and some needs are easier to fix: feeding, diapering, burping, cuddling, and rocking to sleep. However, when your baby continues to cry after you've tried everything you can to calm him, you can feel like a parenting failure. It is harder to bond with an upset baby, because there aren't as many calm moments to enjoy each other's company.

What most breastfeeding moms don't realize is that what you eat can actually influence your baby's disposition.[1] If your baby is fussy during the day, especially just before bedtime, it is entirely possible that some of the foods you are eating are irritating your baby's digestive system.

This book was written to help new parents figure out the reason for their baby's discomfort, because a happy baby is more comfortable in his body and better able to bond securely with the people in his life. If a new mother can calm her baby by changing her diet on a short-term basis, the entire household is able to relax and just *be*. The relationship between the baby's parents becomes less stressful and life with their new baby more enjoyable.[2,3,4]

The Road to Discovery

With my first baby, I needed a few months of practice before breastfeeding felt consistently comfortable. After Cody and I mastered the mechanics of a good latch and my milk supply was well established, I really enjoyed our breastfeeding time together. I liked the closeness that we shared and the feel of a baby that slides off the breast, drunk with milk and fast asleep.

It wasn't always that easy.

14

After Cody was born, like all new parents, my husband and I participated in a 24/7 crash course on baby care. We did our best, and for the most part we did well. (Sometimes, not so well.) What we found most difficult and frustrating was that Cody usually cried on and off between 5:30 and midnight every night.

We walked with Cody, held him, burped him, changed him, and everything else we could think of, but nothing helped to calm him down completely. I kept up with breastfeeding and tried my best, but it was clear that Cody was simply *uncomfortable.* Every night just past midnight, he would FINALLY fall asleep and my husband and I would stumble off to bed, exhausted and incredibly frustrated. It felt like we were missing something important, but no one could tell us what we needed to do to help Cody feel better. He did eventually outgrow his fussy time at night, and we continued to breastfeed for more than a year; however, I always felt I should have been able to relieve his discomfort sooner.

A few years later we had our second baby, Kayla. This time I was more experienced and better prepared for breastfeeding. From some of the studying that I had done for the prenatal class that Judith and I were preparing at that time, I discovered that eliminating specific foods from my diet could potentially make a difference. So, I tried it. When I eliminated certain foods, we noticed immediate results. Kayla was a calm, happy baby and she fussed for about 30 minutes each night. THIRTY MINUTES A NIGHT! We were ecstatic. We enjoyed our evenings as a family, and everyone slept better than we did before.

Now, one could point out that my husband and I were more experienced parents, because we had learned most of our lessons the first time around. While certainly true, it doesn't explain that when I mistakenly ate a sandwich that had hot pepper flakes in it, Kayla was miserable and cried inconsolably later in the day and into the night. It was then that I knew without question that a breastfeeding baby's temperament can be related to the foods that his mother eats.

It was even easier for our third baby, Amanda. Everyone noticed how calm she was, and she was also a happy little thing. She usually had a good 10-minute growl every night before bedtime – and that was it! However, if I ate something that I shouldn't have, she would become fussy and ill-tempered for about a day, until what I had eaten was eliminated from my breastmilk.

There Are Many Reasons Why Your Baby Could Be Fussy

When babies cry a lot in their first months of life, most people call that colic. The term "colic" is defined as unexplained irritability, fussing, and crying for a prolonged period, often at the same time of day, in the early months of life.[5]

Personally, I don't like the term "colic" because it suggests that babies just cry for no apparent reason. My thoughts on colic are that when a baby cries for long periods, it is important to figure out why.

In my practice, I treat a lot of uncomfortable babies throughout my day. I have babies come to me as new patients who cry excessively, who do not latch well at the breast, who are not pooping regularly, who don't sleep well, and who fuss and cry at night. I find that most cry excessively because they are *physically uncomfortable,* and there are three main reasons for a baby's physical discomfort:

1. Physical pain
2. Constipation
3. Problems with digestion

If I can figure out the reason for the pain, and if I can relieve it, the baby can then relax and the crying decreases dramatically.

I'm often asked "Why would a baby need to see a chiropractor? They are just a baby, not even walking yet. What could possibly be wrong with him?" Well, let's explore birth from the baby's point of view.

Just for a moment, I'd like you to imagine being folded up and stuck inside a sleeping bag for nine months and not being able to stretch out at all. At first, the sleeping bag fits you quite well, but throughout those nine months, your sleeping bag gradually becomes tighter and tighter, and you have less room to move around. Now imagine muscles squeezing you from all around your body as you are pushed through your mother's bony pelvis. This passage forces your head bones to slide on top of each other so that you can fit inside this tube as you get pushed through toward the other end. Then imagine that just as you start to come out of that tube, someone grabs your head and forcibly pulls you out. Do you think that you would have a sore neck or body after that process? That is birth for most babies.

Now imagine that you are unable to tell your loved ones where it hurts.

It is my experience that many babies do experience physical pain after birth and they fuss and cry to let us know about it. Newborns sometimes can't turn their necks in full range of motion; they sometimes pull back from the breast when they start to feed. They sometimes have jaws that hurt them and are unable to latch properly.

Many mothers bring their babies to me (or pediatric-focused chiropractors like me), especially if their babies are fussy and won't settle. It's my job to figure out what is the cause of the baby's discomfort and to help their baby feel more comfortable. For the most part, if the reason for the baby's discomfort is a physical one, I can help a fussy baby feel better and sleep better, which provides tremendous relief for everyone in the new family. If I can't find a reason for physical pain, we then start to look at what is in the breastfeeding mother's diet (more on that later...).

What is a pediatric-focused chiropractor?

The International Pediatric Chiropractic Association (ICPA) is a nonprofit organization whose mission is to advance chiropractic by establishing evidence informed practice, supporting excellence in professional skills and delivering educational resources to the public. It fulfills this mission by engaging and serving family chiropractors worldwide through research, training and public education.[6]

Through courses taught by ICPA instructors, pediatric focused chiropractors learn the Webster Technique to help pregnant moms keep their pelvis in the most optimal position for labor and birth. We are taught how to assess and adjust newborns and children, and we learn incredibly gentle adjusting techniques. Many chiropractors take courses with the ICPA and attain certified and diplomate status, which is recognized in the US but not in Canada (that's a long story).

If you would like to have your baby assessed by a pediatric focused chiropractor, I would suggest starting with the ICPA's website at www.icpa4kids.org and click on The ICPA Member Directory button to find a pediatric focused chiropractor close to you. Look first for chiropractors who are certified (CACCP) or have diplomate status (DACCP) on the ICPA site. If there are none of these chiropractors listed close to you, look for chiropractors who are Webster certified, as they have an interest in pregnancy and pediatrics.

If there aren't chiropractors close to you listed on the ICPA website, ask friends and family which chiropractors in your area care for pregnant women and children and schedule a consultation interview for the chiropractors in those clinics. You should be given a 15 minute appointment where you can speak with the chiropractor to ask questions about your baby's condition, and about their experience in treating babies and children. Choose the clinic where you feel most comfortable, and then schedule your first appointment.

Common Reasons a Baby Can Experience Physical Pain

Here are the most likely scenarios of physical pain that babies present with in my clinic. I've outlined how the babies behave, what is the cause of the pain and how to help the baby feel better.

Pulling off the breast in pain

When you feed your baby, he pulls back from the breast and cries, seemingly in pain from both breasts, or just one breast. Your baby becomes angry and frustrated because he is hungry and it hurts him to breastfeed.

In this scenario, there are three likely reasons for your baby to feel physical discomfort:

1. **The joints in his upper neck are irritated and sore**. This is called a facet joint irritation, where the neck joints are stuck and irritated, the upper neck muscles pull tight to protect the neck joints and your baby feels pain when he moves his head, especially in one direction.

2. **He has congenital torticollis** (sometimes called wry neck). Torticollis is caused by a muscle spasm of the sternocleidomastoid (SCM) muscle, which runs from behind the back of the ear, forward and down the neck to the inner collar bone, right where it meets at the breast bone. The SCM becomes so tight it can't relax, and your baby will only look in one direction.
   Congenital torticollis is very common after difficult birth.[7] If your baby is experiencing torticollis, he needs to be assessed and treated as soon as possible by your pediatrician, a pediatric focused chiropractor or physiotherapist.[8,9] Long standing torticollis can pull your baby's head bones out of alignment, causing an asymmetrical head shape. An asymmetry in the facial bones can make the act of sucking more difficult and increases the chance that your baby won't be able to breastfeed easily.[10, 11]

3. **He has a sore jaw** (TMJ – temporomandibular joint dysfunction) – many babies do have painful TMJs after birth and can experience pain when opening and closing their jaw to suck at the breast.

A sore neck and jaw create problems with breastfeeding because every time your baby tries to breastfeed, he feels pain in his neck, his jaw or both, and pulls back from the breast because of it. Your baby becomes quite upset because he is still hungry, but feeding hurts.

Solution

I am biased to my own profession. Pediatric focused chiropractors are very effective at helping to relieve both irritated neck joints, neck muscles in spasm, congenital torticollis, and TMJ pain. We use gentle techniques to release muscle spasm and gentle adjustments to improve joint motion to help your baby move his neck in full range of motion and feel better.[12][13][14][15]

It depends on the severity of the case as to how quickly your baby's condition will improve. Some babies only need a few adjustments to have full, free range of motion restored to their neck. Other babies have difficulties releasing the SCM muscle tension and they need more treatments to find relief. The rate of progress is really up to the baby, and how much tension and pain the baby was in to start with. Usually during treatment, you should notice gradual improvement in his neck range of motion and his level of fussiness.

Your baby has difficulty with his latch

If your baby is having difficulties latching on your breast, and if you are experiencing consistent pain with breastfeeding, your baby might be experiencing

1. A sore jaw or TMJ dysfunction (already discussed)
2. A tongue tie
3. A lip tie

Tongue and lip ties occur when the tissue that tethers the tongue or the lip to the floor of the mouth is too thick. The baby has difficulty sticking out his tongue, which decreases his ability to form a proper latch.[16]

There are many symptoms that can manifest in both mother and baby, when the baby has a tongue or lip tie:[17]

Moms may experience:

- nipple pain and/or erosions
- painful breasts
- low milk supply
- plugged ducts
- mastitis
- frustration, disappointment, and discouragement with breastfeeding
- untimely weaning

Babies may experience:

- poor latch and suck
- clicking sound while nursing (poor suction)
- ineffective milk transfer
- inadequate weight gain or weight loss
- irritability or colic
- fussiness and frequent arching away from the breast
- fatigue within one to two minutes of beginning to nurse
- difficulty establishing suction to maintain a deep grasp on the breast
- gradual sliding off the breast
- "chewing" of the nipple
- falling asleep at the breast having taken less than an optimal feed

Solution

If you or your baby are experiencing any of the above-mentioned symptoms, have your baby assessed by your pediatrician for tongue and/or lip tie. If one is found, your options and solution will be determined by you and your pediatrician.

If a tongue or lip-tie is not found, please have your baby's jaw assessed by a pediatric-focused chiropractor for TMJ dysfunction.

Your baby cries when you lay him flat on his back, or when he's in his car seat

Your baby does not sleep comfortably in his crib, he cries when you lie him on his back and he wakes up often during the night, seemingly in pain. Your baby cries during diaper changes or when you put him in his car seat. He wants to be held all the time.

In this scenario, there are two likely reasons for a baby to feel discomfort:

1. **The joints of the midback between your baby's shoulder blades are fixed and irritated**. I often find that many newborns have irritated joints in their midbacks (the thoracic spine) just between the shoulder blades. The babies who do experience discomfort in this area of the spine cannot get comfortable when they lie flat on their back. They fuss when they are put on their back to sleep. Many of these babies do not like sitting in their car seats because the straps pull them tight to their seat, and puts pressure on their irritated midback joints.

2. **One of your baby's collar bones has been injured or even fractured**. An injured or fractured collar bone can happen during birth, especially if one or both of your baby's shoulders were stuck in the birth canal, and he was forcibly pulled out. These babies do not like it when one arm is lifted, and they don't tend to move the affected arm as much as the other one. Sitting in the car seat can cause extreme pain because the shoulder harnesses put pressure against the collar bone itself.

Solution

If one of your baby's arms is not moving as easily as the other, start with a thorough assessment by your pediatrician to rule out a collar bone fracture. If there is no indication of collar bone pain, and your baby's arms move in all directions freely and easily, an assessment and adjustment of your baby's midback by a pediatric focused chiropractor can get the fixed joints moving and provide relief.

Your baby is not pooping well

Babies should poop often. Anything less than once a day can cause discomfort as we all have experienced if we become backed up ourselves. Some of my moms have come to me with a baby that has not pooped in over a week. A week!! Can you imagine how uncomfortable this little one would feel?

Babies who are constipated exhibit straining, pain with passing stool, pebble-like stool, or streaks of blood. There are many causes of constipation, ranging from the food that the baby is eating (breastmilk or formula), dehydration, intestinal disorders, food allergy, side effects of medication, and family stress.[18]

Solution

From a spine and nervous system point of view, if there is misalignment of the baby's pelvis and sacrum, the nerves that supply the rectum and anus might not function properly and your baby's ability to poop becomes less than optimal. Clinically, chiropractic adjustments help constipated babies to have increased and improved bowel movements.[19] [20] [21] [22]

Pediatric chiropractors assess a baby's spine and sacrum for improper alignment, abnormal movement and excessive muscle tension. With regards to constipation, chiropractors focus on the S2-4 segments of the sacrum to improve nerve function to the bowel and anus.[23]

Many times after adjustments, babies have huge bowel movements, which is a relief to all concerned.

Your baby cries throughout the evening and won't stop

Well, here we are at the reason for this book. This is my personal experience – the scenario where what a breastfeeding mom eats can create discomfort for her baby.

As your baby grows and develops inside your womb, he is constantly fed nutrients and fluids through his umbilical cord. After birth, with the onset of breastfeeding, your baby begins to digest breastmilk for the first time. While colostrum and breastmilk provide the perfect food for your baby's needs, they also contain small particles of everything that a breastfeeding mother eats and drinks.[24] Some babies can experience adverse reactions to specific food particles in the breastmilk as either food allergy or food intolerance.[25]

Food Allergy

Babies can have food allergies to components in their breastmilk or formula. When a person has an allergic reaction to a food protein (called an allergen), his immune system mistakes that food protein for a foreign invader. His body takes steps to protect itself, which involves creating IgE antibodies, which then cause a release of chemicals called histamines that produce the negative effects of an allergic reaction.[26]

A food allergy is a quick reaction that creates uncomfortable symptoms. The effects of food allergies can be noticed within 30 minutes to two hours after breastmilk consumption. Symptoms can include: nausea, vomiting, abdominal pain, diarrhea, hives, asthma, eczema, runny nose, and colic.[27] The types of foods most commonly associated with allergic reactions are: cow's milk, eggs or egg whites, wheat, peanuts, nuts, soy, shellfish, corn, citrus fruits, tomatoes, and spices such as cinnamon or pepper.[28]

It is recommended that a baby with a predisposition toward allergies be exclusively breastfed for the first six months of life and that breastfeeding be continued for at least the first year, if not longer.[29]

Food Intolerance

Food intolerance is slower to show symptoms and more difficult to figure out. When a person has an intolerance to a certain food, his digestive system becomes irritated and he is not able to digest that food very easily. The effects of the discomfort take longer to manifest – they can become evident over a period of hours to days after ingesting the food itself. The symptoms for food intolerance are: diarrhea, gas, abdominal distention, abdominal pain, bloody stools, vomiting, feeding refusal, eczema, stuffy nose, coughing, and wheezing.[30] [31]

If a breastfeeding baby has food intolerance to something in his breastmilk, figuring out exactly which food is creating the problems can be difficult, as the baby becomes fussy hours to days after breastfeeding (and the mother may have eaten many different foods by then).

The Foods That Most Commonly Cause a Baby Discomfort

Everyone is different when it comes to digesting food, and babies are no different than adults. Some of us can eat all foods with no problem, while some of us have troubles digesting specific foods and spices.

The following is a list of the most common foods that have created problems for my own babies and for the babies of my patients. When you are reading this list, please do not panic. You will not have to eliminate all of these foods at once. We will very soon explain our relatively easy food elimination diet that you can follow to determine which foods are creating your baby's fussiness.

Our top 15 list of foods that can create discomfort for babies through their breastmilk are:

1. Cow's Milk and Dairy Products

2. Peppers

3. Cruciferous Vegetables—Cabbage, Cauliflower, and Broccoli

4. Onions

5. Tomatoes

6. Dried Beans

7. Oranges

8. Eggs

9. Peanuts and Tree Nuts

10. Wheat

11. Soy

12. Corn

13. Chocolate

14. Cinnamon

15. Strawberries

Now let's talk about why these foods cause problems for babies and what you can do to help. Some of these foods have been scientifically researched, some are listed through practical experience. I have listed them in the order that I found works best when helping my breastfeeding moms.

Cow's Milk and Dairy Products

Cow's milk is the most common cause of food allergy in infants and young children.[32] [33] [34] Many medical studies have shown that dairy products can cause colicky symptoms for babies, whether from the breastmilk of mothers who drink cow's milk[35] [36] [37] [38] [39] [40] or from cow's milk formula.[41] [42] [43] [44]

Cow's milk proteins are much larger than human milk proteins and can be found in the breastmilk of women who drink milk or eat dairy products. Because of their size, cow's milk proteins can be quite difficult for babies to digest and can cause excessive spit-up, vomiting, diarrhea, gas, and distended, painful belly.

Peppers

Many babies do not do well with the pepper family.[45] Red, green, orange, and yellow peppers, jalapeño peppers, pepper flakes, and spices.

Cruciferous Vegetables

Cabbage, cauliflower, and broccoli are the most distressing of the cruciferous vegetables for a baby.[46] [47]

The remaining cruciferous vegetables can cause colicky symptoms when breastfeeding mothers eat them. They are: arugula, bok choy, brussels sprouts, collard greens, kale, mustard greens, radish, turnip, and watercress. However, for the beginning of our food elimination diet, we will focus only on the cabbage, cauliflower, and broccoli.

Onions

Onions can create problems for some babies.[48] Cooked onions are usually tolerated better than raw onions.

Tomatoes

The carotene from tomatoes that forms in breastmilk is called lycopene.[49] Tomatoes also contain nicotine,[50] which could be another cause of a breastfeeding baby's discomfort. Many babies have problems if their mothers eat tomatoes, or tomato-based sauces, salsas, or soups.

Dried Beans

Beans are gas-forming and can cause a baby to become really uncomfortable. Baked beans, black beans, kidney beans, pinto beans, etc. should be avoided.

Oranges

Oranges, orange juice, or orange zest can create fussiness in some babies. Sometimes when women remove dairy from their diets, they supplement with calcium-enriched orange juice. There have been too many incidences of fussy babies after orange juice is consumed to ignore it.

Please note: I didn't notice that my babies had difficulties with the other citrus fruits – lemons, limes, grapefruit – but that could be a possibility for some babies.

Eggs

When a breastfeeding mom eats eggs, the protein ovalbumin shows up in her breastmilk, which can cause problems for some babies.[51]

Wheat

Wheat allergy is lower on the list of allergenic proteins that show up in breastmilk.[52] However, wheat proteins do create problems for many people, and babies could certainly be affected by them. If you are already eating gluten-free, then your baby is as well.

Peanuts and Tree Nuts

Nuts are a great source of healthy fat and protein. They can also be the most controversial foods for pregnant and breastfeeding moms to eat because of potential nut allergies. Please note that peanuts are legumes, not nuts, because they grow underground. Peanuts are also more allergenic than tree nuts (almonds, walnuts, pecans, cashews).

If a peanut or nut allergy is a concern in your or your partner's family, please consult with your medical doctor and/or your allergist to carefully consider whether you will eat nuts while pregnant and breastfeeding.

If there are no allergies to peanuts and tree nuts on either side of your family, eating nuts during breastfeeding could be a good thing, and here's why:

A groundbreaking study released in the *New England Journal of Medicine*[53] recommends that babies should be fed peanuts between months four and six, to help their bodies desensitize to peanut proteins. These recommendations are quite revolutionary, as health providers have been counseling breastfeeding moms to avoid peanuts throughout breastfeeding, and that babies not be fed peanuts for at least their first year.

This new study's conclusion is that babies who are exposed to peanuts earlier in their lives have less chance of developing an allergy to peanuts!!!

As long as there are no allergies to peanuts or tree nuts on either side of the family, pregnant women and breastfeeding women should include peanuts and nuts in their diet. If you eat these foods, you safely expose your baby to peanut and tree nut proteins, and possibly avoid allergy in the long term. For more information on this new finding, please visit **www.niaid.nih.gov** and search for "peanut allergy."

Again, if you or your partner do have allergies in your families to peanuts or tree nuts, please consult with your medical doctor or an allergist before adding these foods to your diet.

Soy Products

If you are eating or drinking soy products, be aware that your baby may be one of the small percentage of babies who have troubles digesting soy.[54]

Corn

Corn is lower on the list of allergens. However, it creates digestive problems for a lot of people, and your baby could be one of them.

Chocolate

Some babies have troubles with chocolate.[55] [56]

Cinnamon

Cinnamon can be problematic for some babies.[57]

Strawberries

Some moms have noticed that strawberries create fussiness for their babies.

How to Get Started
on Your Food Elimination Diet

Jack Newman suggests in his *Guide to Breastfeeding*[58] that breastfeeding moms eliminate one food for three weeks, and wait to see what happens. Then, they can move on to the next food, and wait three weeks to see what happens after that. My thoughts on this method are: Sure, you could eliminate foods that way, but it might take months to figure out which foods are problematic and, in the meantime, you're left with a baby in severe discomfort.

After one week of having my baby cry nonstop from 5 to 11 every night, I would have done anything to make things better. It seems to me that giving up some foods for a month is a small price to pay to make a difference quickly.

I have discovered, from my own experience and from that of my breastfeeding patients, that there is a relatively easy food elimination diet to calm your fussy baby. This is the breastfeeding diet that I give to my moms in my practice:

Week 1—Start with Just Dairy

Dairy is the most allergenic protein found in breastmilk, and it is the food most likely to create discomfort for a breastfeeding baby.[59 60 61 62] Start with eliminating dairy products completely from your diet and wait for one week to see if your baby's fussiness decreases.

You must eliminate all dairy products from your diet: milk, butter, cheese, yogurt, cottage cheese, sour cream, ice cream, cream-based soups and sauces. Many processed foods contain dairy, especially baked goods and potato products. Check the labels of all prepared foods that you are eating to see if they contain the following by-products of milk: whey, casein, and lactalbumin.

There are many tasty dairy-free options to be found in grocery stores and health food stores, such as:

1. Coconut milk, coconut yogurt, and coconut coffee creamer. Please note: Some coconut yogurts are awesome, some are terrible. Our favorite brand is YOSO.

2. Almond milk, almond yogurt. Almond milk is a great non-dairy choice, and it goes great with cereal.

3. Cashew milk, cashew yogurt, cashew milk ice cream. Cashew milk is my daughter's favorite, both vanilla and chocolate.

4. Rice milk, rice milk ice cream.

5. Soy milk, soy coffee creamer. These are the least-great choices when it comes to breastfeeding. Soy products are linked to estrogen-mimicking symptoms and some babies have difficulties digesting soy.[63]

Weeks 2 and 3 – Eliminate the Top Seven Foods

If your baby is still fussy after the end of the first week of eliminating just dairy, then it's time to eliminate the top seven irritating foods from your diet. Wait for two more weeks, and see if your baby's fussiness decreases.

Here are the top seven foods to eliminate next:

1. **Cow's Milk and Dairy Products** – Continue to eliminate dairy products from your diet.

2. **Peppers** – Red, green, orange, and yellow peppers, jalapeño peppers, pepper flakes, and spices. Be careful of peppers of all kinds, spice blends that contain peppers, salsas, BBQ chips,

BBQ sauces, hot sauces, chili pepper, etc. A bit of black pepper sprinkled in a big recipe is usually fine, but if your baby remains fussy after a few weeks of avoiding these foods, forego the use of black pepper as well.

3. **Cruciferous Vegetables** – Cabbage, cauliflower, and broccoli.

4. **Onions** – I found that raw onions caused my babies discomfort, but cooked onions were easily tolerated.

5. **Tomatoes** – Raw tomatoes, ketchup, tomato sauces, tomato soup, salsa, tomato paste, ketchup, and "all dressed" flavored potato chips.

6. **Dried Beans** – Baked beans, black beans, kidney beans, pinto beans, chick peas, etc.

7. **Oranges** – Anything with oranges, orange juice, or orange zest.

Week 4+ – Eliminate the Last Eight Foods (Only if necessary!)

Hopefully after you have eliminated the top seven foods, you will notice a reduction in your baby's fussiness. Your baby might become completely calm. If that's the case, then don't take anything more out of your diet. Stay right where you are.

If your baby is still gassy and fussy, you can eliminate the eight remaining foods all at once, or try the food that you think might be more likely than the others. If you are eating a lot of one of the following foods, chances are that is the food that's creating the problem.

1. **Eggs** – We do include eggs in some of our recipes. There are commercial egg replacement products available in grocery stores and health food stores. It is best to consult with someone in your area as products differ from region to region.

2. **Wheat** – You may need to go gluten-free. Substitute all wheat flour products with gluten-free ones, but the good news is there are many wonderful gluten-free substitutes, such as brown rice pasta, rice crackers and gluten free breads.

3. **Peanuts and Tree Nuts** – Check labels on granola bars, cookies, protein bars, etc. All processed and packaged food labels must indicate if peanuts and tree nuts could be contained. If you are eating out, be careful of salads, breaded foods, sauces, desserts, and baked goods. Asian and Mexican foods can contain nuts. Ice cream parlors use nuts for toppings, which can cross-contaminate other products. Be sure to ask about which foods might contain peanuts and tree nuts. Most restaurants will be prepared with a list of foods that are safe.

4. **Soy Products** – Avoid soy milk, soy coffee creamer, soy yogurt or ice cream, edamame, miso, tempeh, and tofu. Soy can also be found in canned broths, soups, chicken nuggets, canned tuna, processed meats, hot dogs, nut butters, energy bars, baked goods, and many other processed foods. Asian cuisine contains a lot of soy ingredients.[64]

5. **Corn** – If you think corn could be an irritating food for your baby, you will need to eliminate corn, corn syrup, corn flour, corn vegetable oil, maize.

Corn and corn-derived products are found in a wide variety of packaged foods, including: cereals, candies, jams, syrups, sauces, snack foods, canned fruits, prepared meats, such as hot dogs and deli meats, and some beverages.[65]

Many food ingredients can contain corn: baking powder, caramel, cellulose, citric acid, dextrin, dextrose, inositol, malt, maltodextrin, monosodium glutamate (MSG), semolina, sodium erythorbate, sorbitol, starch, vanilla extract, xanthan gum, and xylitol. Check with a product's manufacturer if you have any questions about an ingredient's origin.

1. **Chocolate** – This just isn't fair, is it?

2. **Cinnamon** – Check your ingredients list in baked goods, granolas, and protein bars.

3. **Strawberries** – Strawberries might be included in some fruit juices, fruit leather, granolas, energy bars, popsicles, and

sorbets. Check the label if you are eating or drinking anything fruity.

Added Nutritional Support

As a breastfeeding mother, it is important that you consume the recommended levels of vitamins and minerals for both you and your baby. During your food elimination diet, please take a high-quality multivitamin that includes calcium, magnesium, and vitamin D. You may want to add an additional calcium supplement, depending on if you are substituting almond and cashew milk for cow's milk or just eliminating dairy completely from your diet.

In practice, I recommend that my breastfeeding patients continue to take their prenatal vitamins for as long as they are breastfeeding.

What to Do If Your Baby Is Still Fussy

It takes at least one week for your breastmilk to be entirely clear of some foods.[66] Many breastfeeding professionals are suggesting to wait for three weeks of food elimination to determine if the foods that you are eating are creating your baby's discomfort.[67] If you have eliminated all of the 15 foods from your diet for three weeks and your baby is still fussy, there are several things you can do:

Have you had your baby checked by a pediatric-focused chiropractor?

If your baby's fussiness has not changed after a month of eliminating the top seven or the top 15 foods from your diet, there is another reason for the discomfort and it is most likely a physical one. If you haven't already done so, make an appointment with a pediatric focused chiropractor – we can determine the reason for physical pain and help alleviate it.

Keep a food diary

If your baby remains fussy, and you think that an additional food is involved, other than the top 15, it's time to start a food diary.

Purchase a small notebook that you can easily carry in your purse. On the pages of your food diary, divide each page into three vertical columns. Label column one TIME, column two FOOD, and column three FUSSINESS.

When you eat something, make note of the time of your meal or snack in the first column and everything that you ate or drank in the middle column. When your baby is fussy or crying, mark down in the third column the time your baby started crying and for how long he cried.

Look for any patterns between eating or drinking a certain food and when your baby cries. Remember, with food allergies, the adverse reactions happen quite quickly after your baby breastfeeds. With food intolerance, the adverse effects could become evident in anywhere from a few hours to a few days after your baby's feed. It might take weeks to notice a pattern with the timing of eating a specific food and your baby beginning to fuss.

If you discover a pattern, eliminate that food from your diet and wait one to three weeks to see if your baby's fussiness decreases.

Pay special attention to whether your baby is fussy after you eat:

- Grapefruit, lemons, or limes.
- The remaining cruciferous vegetables. Are you eating any arugula, bok choy, brussels sprouts, collard greens, kale, mustard greens, radish, turnip, or watercress? If so, remove them from your diet and see if it helps.
- Cooked onions.
- Black pepper.

Check the labels of prepared foods that you are eating

- If you are drinking a blended fruit juice, make sure that there is no orange or strawberry juice in the ingredients list.

- Look for whey, casein, lactalbumin, or modified dairy products in the ingredients list of all the prepared foods that you are eating. Note: Many frozen potato products have dairy additives to improve their taste.

- Prepared foods that are said to be "non-dairy" or "dairy-free" can contain dairy protein. The most likely protein is casein.[68]

- Sometimes companies list "spices" in their ingredients, but there is no way of knowing which individual spices they use. A "secret spice blend" in a pre-packaged food could contain pepper or pepper flakes.

When You Should Introduce These Foods Back Into Your Diet

Between three and four months of age, a baby's digestive system is almost fully mature[69] and can usually tolerate a wider variety of foods. (If your baby was over four months old when you started your food elimination diet, and is calmer because of it, wait at least a month to start food challenges.)

Of course, we want you to eat a full and varied diet. The problem is how to determine which foods are tolerated by your baby, and which ones aren't. The only way for you to know for sure is to challenge each food individually.

What is a Food Challenge?

A food challenge is when you choose one food to experiment with, eat a small amount, and wait at least 24 hours to see how your baby reacts. If your baby has the same temperament and all is well, add that food back into your diet and gradually increase the portion size.

Introduce new foods slowly (one food every week or so) in order to easily identify which foods your baby can tolerate. If you notice that your baby is fussier, cries differently, or seems to be in pain, your baby is not ready for this food at this time. Wait a month or more and try again with the same food.

How long does it take for a baby to stop being fussy?

Well, that's the million-dollar question. Every baby is different. Some calm down immediately after you start your elimination diet. Others continue to fuss, and it takes more time to figure out which foods are creating their difficulties.

The bottom line: do what you can to calm your baby by following our elimination diet. Then, when your baby is calm and has been for at least a month, pick one food and challenge it. Keep track of what works, what doesn't, and when you did your test. If your baby does not tolerate the food you ate, he will be an uncomfortable baby for a few hours, but this is the reality of food challenges.

It is worth the risk of upsetting your baby's digestive system, because your health counts, too! Some of the foods in the top seven might not be a problem at all for your baby. It would be nice to add some of these foods back into your regular diet, so that you can have more variety and your baby can experience these food proteins in your breastmilk. It just takes a food challenge to find out, and then you'll know for sure.

Keep at it. Some challenges will go well; some not so well. Take a break if you need to. There are no rules as to how frequently challenges should be done.

Tips to Soothe a Fussy Baby

While you are on your food elimination diet, here are a few ideas you can try to calm your fussy baby:

Wear your baby

Babies like to feel you close and hear your heartbeat; a baby sling or a baby carrier will support your back and make it easier for you to wear your baby. Newborns aren't able to sit and support their own body weight, so a baby sling works best for the first few months. Once your baby can sit up comfortably, then try a baby carrier.

Dance together

Gentle music soothes babies, rather than fast music with a lively beat. By swaying and humming to the music, you entertain your baby and help him to relax and stop crying. If you can, make a playlist of your favorite slow songs and enjoy some bonding time together.

Swaddle your baby before you rock him to sleep

Newborns like to feel snug and cozy, and swaddling can create that feeling for them. If you'd like more information on how to swaddle a baby, there are many great videos available on YouTube.

Skin-on-skin contact helps

One of the nicest ways to accomplish skin-on-skin contact, especially in the evening, is to run a warm bath, light a few candles, and turn off the lights. Bathing with the baby is an excellent activity for dads/working parents. The primary caregiver usually needs a break at the end of the day, and the working parents don't have much opportunity to hold their babies skin-on-skin.

Simply have your partner sit in the tub, place your naked baby on his or her chest, and cover the baby's back and legs with a warm, wet washcloth. Babies like the feel of the close contact, the warm water, and the soft lights. When Grandma visits, if your partner doesn't want to give up bath time, just have your partner wear his or her swimsuit!

Learn infant massage

Infant massage provides much physical relief for babies. It improves digestion, sleep, relaxation, bonding, and brain stimulation. Check in your community to see if infant massage classes are offered. You can also download the infant massage video that I made for my patients to learn how to massage their babies. It is very low-tech, but it does show you how to do the infant massage strokes and provides handouts that you can use.

Please visit www.awesomemomtips.com/infant-massage-kit.

Walk around the block with baby in the stroller

Especially if you walk on a sidewalk, the rhythmic bumping movement can soothe a baby quickly. You both get some fresh air and you benefit from adding exercise to your day.

Go for an evening drive

Some babies find the hum of a running engine to be calming. I found that if I placed a rolled-up burp cloth on either side of my baby's head and then tucked a blanket firmly around him in his car seat, it helped him to feel more comfortable and secure in the car.

Rock your baby to sleep

If you don't have a rocking chair, get one! Rocking provides gentle movement that can calm a fussy baby. Either hold your baby in the crook of your arm with pillows for support, or hold your baby on your chest as you rock back and forth.

Vacuum the floors of your house

Many babies like the hum of a vacuum. Place your baby in a sling or a baby carrier and vacuum away. If your baby does calm down, you benefit in two ways: you end up with a calm baby and a clean carpet.

Tips to Help Make Breastfeeding Easier

While you are on your food elimination diet, here are a few suggestions for you to make your life easier as a breastfeeding mom.

Set up a breastfeeding station

You can breastfeed in peace if what you need is within arm's reach. Find a restful space and stock it with:

- A comfortable chair and foot stool
- Extra pillows for your back and your lap
- A blanket for you
- A blanket for your baby
- Snacks that you can eat one-handed (see our recipe section for ideas)
- A water bottle, filled and ready to go
- Books to read
- Burp cloths
- A phone charger
- Diapers and wipes

Keep your baby close

I didn't like to wake up from a sound sleep to a hungry, angry, crying baby, and you might feel that way, too. One solution is to keep your baby close to you and feed him as he wakes up. A sleepy baby is relaxed and can latch more easily onto the breast. If you start to breastfeed before he becomes fully awake, you will have extra time to get a proper latch.

Have your baby sleep in the same room with you. Babies make little noises as they wake up. With your baby within hearing distance, you will usually respond to these noises in your sleep and you wake up as he does. You have extra time to go to the bathroom and to get a drink

41

of water before you begin your next breastfeeding session. If you start breastfeeding before your baby fully wakes, you'll have extra time to get a proper latch.

Make dinner early

Make your dinner in the morning, when everyone is happy and you have more energy. Often, new moms battle through meal preparation when their baby is crying, and dinner becomes a resentful occasion that no one enjoys. Many new families skip dinner all together, or eat something less nutritious. However, if you have your supper prepared and ready to pop in the oven, or you have a slow-cooked meal or a pot of soup on the stove, you can care for your fussy baby in the late afternoon and early evening while your dinner cooks. When you find an opportunity to eat, your food will be hot and waiting for you.

Let your girls go free

When you are home, take off your nursing bra. Hanging loose provides relief and can help you avoid mastitis (an infection of a plugged milk duct in your breast). You might leak a bit, but at home it won't matter so much; you can just change into a dry shirt.

Note: Choose nursing bras that DO NOT have underwires. An underwire in a nursing bra can compress the milk ducts along the outside of the breast and contribute to mastitis for some women.

Put something of yours in your baby's crib

Keep the shirt that you slept in and place it beside your baby when he naps. Babies sleep better if they can smell their mother close.[70]

Our Breastfeeding-Friendly Recipes

Before We Get Started

To gluten or not to gluten

Some recipes in this book call for flour, which you can substitute with gluten-free flour.

If you are already gluten-free, then you know the ins and outs of gluten-free flour, and may already have a favorite brand handy. If you are new to gluten-free cooking, try a few different gluten-free flours to find the one that you like best. There are lots of great websites to check out if you are looking for ideas and instructions on how to get started.

Let's talk about oil

We all have our own favorite oils to cook with. Some are great for cooking, some are better left raw. Personally, I like cooking with avocado oil. You might like cooking with coconut oil or grapeseed oil. To make this easier on all of us, I will just use the term "oil" and you choose the one you like best.

Let's talk about garlic

In my recipes, when I am cooking with garlic, I use a garlic press. Some of you might not have one, so I decided to use the term "minced garlic," meaning that you chop it up as finely as you can. If you have a garlic press, please use it!

Nuts again

If you are avoiding nuts in your diet, please remove them from our recipes.

Tips to Convert Your Favorite Recipes into Breastfeeding-Friendly Ones

Pasta

Most pasta sauces are either tomato- or cream-based, and both o' these options are not breastfeeding-friendly. If you are making a pasta sauce for your family, prepare your meat and vegetables as usual, and then set aside your portion before you add the tomato- or cream-based sauce for everyone else.

Place your meat and vegetables in a large, non-stick frying pan with two or three tablespoons of oil and stir-fry until cooked through. Add your portion of the pasta, and continue cooking until browned and sizzling. Pasta cooked this way is actually quite tasty — we still hea' up our leftovers this way, and my children are teenagers now.

Baked Goods

Depending on which foods you are eliminating from your diet, you car modify your favorite recipes by substituting:

- apple juice for milk, and applesauce for yogurt or sour cream
- commercial egg replacement products for eggs
- gluten-free flours for wheat flour

Citrus Fruits

Substitute lemons or limes in your recipes that call for orange pieces orange zest, or orange juice. If your baby is still fussy after this substitution, remove citrus entirely from your diet.

HIGH ENERGY
SNACKS

Snack ideas that you don't have to cook

- **Almonds and raisins**. You can mix these yourself beforehand and keep them in convenient snacking locations throughout the house.

- **Fresh fruits** can be washed and/or cut and placed at your breastfeeding station to snack on while breastfeeding.

- **Dried fruits** such as raisins, dates, cranberries, apricots, figs, peaches, pears, apricots, and apples can be placed in strategic places around your house.

- **Protein bars.** Protein bars are a better snack option than granola bars, because the extra protein keeps your blood sugars more even. Many protein bars are dairy-free, such as Clif Bar, ProBar Meal, and Larabar. Make sure you read the ingredients list before you purchase protein bars. They are nutritious AND expensive and you don't want to choose the wrong type. Additionally, check out your local health food store to see what's available in your area.

- **Veggies and dip.** Prepare breastfeeding-friendly vegetables and keep them in your fridge, ready to munch on when you're hungry. There are many vegetables to choose from: carrots, celery, cucumber, zucchini slices, green beans, baby corn, and mushrooms. Most dips contain dairy products or pepper spices, but the following guacamole recipe works well.

Guacamole Dip

Makes 8 servings

2 ripe avocados
2 tbsp. mayonnaise
1 tbsp. fresh cilantro, finely chopped
3 tbsp. fresh lime juice
½ tsp. salt

Mash up the avocado with a fork. Add the rest of the ingredients and stir well.

Per serving: 95 calories, 0.8 g protein, 3.7 g carbohydrates, 9.2 g total fat, 2.9 g fiber, 1.3 g saturated fat, 20 mg sodium, 0.12 g sugar.

Hard-Boiled Eggs

Extra protein helps with your blood-sugar levels and eggs are a great source of protein. I used to hard-boil 12 eggs, keep them in the fridge, and then eat them throughout the week when I needed a quick protein snack.

How to Hard-Boil Eggs

1. Add your eggs into a saucepan and cover with water about an inch higher than your eggs in the pot.

2. Set your burner on high and bring to a boil. Once your water boils, reduce the heat to medium-high and let the eggs cook for eight minutes.

3. When done, pour out the hot water, then add cold water to cover the eggs. Let your eggs sit in your sink until they are cool. Place them in the fridge for when you are hungry. Hard-boiled eggs last a week in the fridge.

The Best Granola EVER

16 servings

3 cups oats (large flake oats are better, but any kind will do)
1 cup sunflower seeds
2 cups coarsely chopped whole almonds
1 cup coarsely chopped walnuts
1 cup diced dried apricots
1 cup dried cranberries
1 cup raisins
¼ cup oil
¼ cup brown sugar
½ tsp. cinnamon or cocoa powder

In a large mixing bowl, combine the oats, sunflower seeds and nuts. In a measuring cup, mix the oil, cinnamon or cocoa powder and brown sugar until smooth. Pour over the nuts and oats and mix until well coated, then spread evenly over 2 baking sheets lined with parchment paper. Bake at 350° F convection bake for 10-15 minutes or until the nuts and oats start to brown at the edges. Add the dried fruits evenly over the oat and nut mixture and stir well. Bake for 5 minutes more, then let cool.

The fruit should be warm when you take the baking sheets out of the oven. Watch closely, as the raisins can plump up and burn easily if you bake them for too long. This granola tastes wonderful eaten with coconut yogurt for breakfast.

Per serving: 370 calories, 9 g protein, 41 g carbohydrates, 22.4 g total fat, 2 g saturated fat, 6.5 g fiber, 4 mg sodium, 21.4 g sugar.

Protein Shakes

1 serving

Protein shakes provide instant energy and a great start to your day. They are easy to make and to take with you as you care for your baby.

2 cups almond, cashew or rice milk
1 cup frozen berries or fruit
1 cup ice cubes
¼ cup hemp protein powder

Pour all of the ingredients into a blender and process on high until smooth.

Note: Most protein powders are made from whey or casein (by-products from cow's milk) or soy.

A great alternative for dairy or soy protein powders is hemp protein. You can find hemp protein powder in most health food stores.

Per serving: 316 calories, 20 g protein, 36 g carbohydrates, 11.6 g total fat, 0.6 g saturated fat, 11 g fiber, 316 mg sodium, 15 g sugar.

Honey-Coated Almonds

8 servings

4 cups whole almonds
¼ cup liquid honey
½ tsp. cinnamon or cocoa powder

In a medium-sized bowl, add all ingredients and toss until well coated. Spread the almonds evenly across a baking sheet lined with parchment paper. Bake at 300° F for 10 minutes and stir. Bake for another 5-10 minutes until the nuts are browned at the edges. Watch carefully at this last stage, as nuts burn quickly. Let cool.

Per serving: 410 calories, 15 g protein, 15 g carbohydrates, 35 g total fat, 2.8 g saturated fat, 9 g fiber, 0 mg sodium, 2.8 g sugar.

Ginger-Spiced Mixed Nuts

12 servings

2 tbsp. oil
½ tsp. ginger
½ tsp. cinnamon
¼ cup liquid honey
1 cup coarsely chopped walnut halves
1 cup coarsely chopped pecan halves
2 cups coarsely chopped whole almonds
1 cup raisins

Preheat a large, non-stick frying pan on medium heat. In a measuring cup, mix together the oil, spices and liquid honey until smooth. Pour into the frying pan and heat through. Add the nuts and stir to coat, then add the raisins and stir again. Let cook for 1 minute in the frying pan, stirring constantly. Spread evenly over two baking sheets covered with waxed paper or parchment paper. Let cool.

Per serving: 310 calories, 6.2 g protein, 23 g carbohydrates, 24 g total fat, 2.1 g saturated fat, 4.1 g fiber, 2 mg sodium, 15 g sugar.

Trail Mix

8 servings

1 cup whole almonds
1 cup walnuts coarsely chopped
1 cup pecans
1 cup raisins
1 cup dried cranberries

Mix in a large bowl and store in a resealable freezer bag close to your breastfeeding station.

Per serving: 400 calories, 8 g protein, 37 g carbohydrates, 29 g total fat, 2.4 g saturated fat, 6 g fiber, 3 mg sodium, 24 g sugar.

Maple Mixed Nuts

10 servings

1 cup almonds
1 cup walnuts
1 cup pecans
1 cup cashews
1 cup shelled pumpkin seeds
¼ cup real maple syrup
½ tsp. cinnamon or cocoa powder

In a large bowl, mix the nuts, the cinnamon or cocoa powder and the maple syrup. Spread evenly over a baking sheet lined with parchment paper. Bake at 350° F for 10 minutes, stir well and bake again 5-10 minutes or until the nuts are brown at the edges. Watch carefully at the end stages, as nuts burn easily. Let cool.

Per serving: 370 calories, 9.2 g protein, 20 g carbohydrates, 31 g total fat, 3.5 g saturated fat, 4.1 g fiber, 4.3 mg sodium, 6.7 g sugar.

SANDWICHES

Grilled Peanut Butter and Jelly Sandwiches

One day, I started to make grilled cheese sandwiches, only to discover that the cheese had gone bad. Out of desperation, I chose peanut butter and jelly. It was an instant hit and one you might enjoy as well!

4 Servings

8 slices bread
4 tsp. margarine
6 tbsp. peanut butter
2 tbsp. your favourite jelly

Make peanut butter and jelly sandwiches (use the jelly sparingly as it tends to leak).

Spread a thin layer of margarine on the outside surfaces of your sandwiches

Grill over medium heat on an electric griddle, or frying pan on the stove, until both sides are browned to your liking.

Have extra supplies handy, because everyone wants more!!!

Per serving: 384 calories, 12 g protein, 45 g carbohydrates, 19.5 g total fat, 3.4 g saturated fat, 6 g fiber, 392 mg sodium, 9.6 g sugar.

Monte Cristo Sandwiches

4 servings

This sandwich is another great hit in our house. (When you can go back to eating dairy, add cheese to the inside of the sandwich!)

8 slices bread
8 slices of thinly shaved ham
8 slices of thinly shaved turkey or chicken (or use leftovers from a turkey day)
4 tsp of your favourite jelly OR mustard (see note)
4 eggs
Non-stick cooking spray

Note: traditional Monte Cristo sandwiches are served with jelly, either to dip in, or the jelly is added to the inside of the sandwich. You could do either, or you could add your favourite mustard to the inside of the sandwich to give it a bit of punch.

Heat an electric griddle, or a frying pan on the stove to medium heat. Spray with non-stick cooking spray.

In a wide bowl, beat the eggs.

Make up each sandwich with the 2 slices of ham and 2 slices of turkey – jelly or mustard is optional. Then holding the fully assembled sandwich in your hands, dip each side of the sandwich into the egg mixture like you're making French toast and place on the griddle.

Brown on both sides to your liking.

Per serving: 361 calories, 30 g protein, 36 g carbohydrates, 11.4 g total fat, 3.0 g saturated fat, 4 g fiber, 1.5 g sodium, 2.8 g sugar.

Waldorf Turkey Sandwiches

10 servings

½ cup sunflower seeds
3 cups diced turkey
1 cup diced apples
1 cup minced celery
½ - ¾ cup Miracle Whip or mayonnaise
Sea salt and pepper to taste
10 sliced and toasted buns
Lettuce leaves

Toast the sunflower seeds in a non-stick frying pan over medium-low heat, stirring often as they burn easily. Heat until they are toasted evenly. Remove from the burner and let cool.

In a bowl, combine all of the ingredients except the buns and lettuce and stir until well mixed. Spoon onto toasted buns and top with fresh lettuce.

Per serving: 333 calories, 28 g protein, 27 g carbohydrates, 15 g total fat, 2.2 g saturated fat, 5.6 g fiber, 500 mg sodium, 9 g sugar.

Crab Salad Sandwiches

6 servings

3 cans crabmeat, flaked with cartilage removed
½ cup minced celery
¼ cup minced water chestnuts
1 tsp. dried parsley flakes
2 tsp. lemon juice
½ cup mayonnaise or Miracle Whip
Sea salt and pepper to taste
Lettuce
Kaiser rolls

In a large bowl, mix everything together except for the lettuce and rolls. Split the buns and broil until golden brown. Top with the crabmeat and lettuce.

Per serving: 264 calories, 16 g protein, 14 g carbohydrates, 16 g total fat, 2.67 g saturated fat, 1.4 g fiber, 410 mg sodium, 3 g sugar.

Awesome Tuna Sandwiches

6 servings

2 cans albacore tuna, drained and flaked
½ cup minced dill pickles
½ cup minced celery
1 carrot, peeled and shredded
½ cup Miracle Whip
Alfalfa or bean sprouts
6 sliced and toasted buns

Mix everything except the sprouts and buns into a medium-sized mixing bowl.

Serve with toasted buns and top with the sprouts.

Per serving: 255 calories, 15 g protein, 20 g carbohydrates, 15 g total fat, 2.4 g saturated fat, 5.6 g fiber, 570 mg sodium, 2 g sugar.

SOUPS

Corn Chowder

10 servings

4 cups diced potatoes
3 cups cubed ham
1 cup diced onions
1 cup diced celery
3 cups shredded carrots
2 cans creamed style corn
1 tsp. sea salt
2 bouillon cubes
6 cups water
2 tbsp. parsley flakes
¼ cup flour
½ cup cold water

Peel or scrub the potatoes and cut into bite-sized pieces. Place them in a medium-sized saucepan and cover with water. Place a lid on your pot, bring to a boil and then let the pot sit on low heat until the potatoes are cooked. Drain the water off of the potatoes and add them to the soup.

In a large soup pot, add all of the above ingredients, except for the flour and ½ cup of water. Bring to a boil, reduce the heat, cover and simmer on low for 2-3 hours. Add extra water if necessary to keep the soup from becoming too thick.

30 minutes before eating, mix the flour with ½ cup cold water until smooth. Add the flour mixture to the soup and stir often. Wait 10-15 minutes for the soup to thicken before serving.

Per serving: 250 calories, 13 g protein, 35 g carbohydrates, 6.3 g total fat, 1.8 g saturated fat, 5.2 g fiber, 1.4 g sodium, 7.5 g sugar.

Sausage Chowder

12 servings

10 cups water
2 bouillon cubes
2 lb. sausages – we use the honey garlic sausages from Costco
2 cups diced onions
3 cups diced carrots
3 cups diced celery
3 cups diced apples – you can leave the peel on if you like
1 tsp. salt
1 tsp. black pepper
1 tsp. cumin
1 tsp. coriander
2 tbsp. parsley flakes
5 cups diced potatoes

In a large soup pot, add the water and bouillon cubes and let simmer over medium-high heat. Cut the sausage skins and drop the sausage meat onto a hot frying pan. Break up the sausage meat into little pieces and fry until done. Add to the soup pot.

In the same frying pan, cook the onions, carrots and celery in the sausage drippings until partially cooked, then add to the soup. Add the apples and the spices.

Peel or scrub the potatoes and cut into bite-sized pieces. Place them in a medium-sized saucepan and cover with water. Place a lid on your pot, bring to a boil and then let the pot sit on low heat until the potatoes are cooked. Drain the water off of the potatoes and add them to the soup.

Cover and let simmer for 2-3 hours, stirring often. Add more water if the soup becomes too thick.

Per serving: 284 calories, 13 g protein, 21 g carbohydrates, 16 g total fat, 8.5 g saturated fat, 4 g fiber, 1.4 g sodium, 5.5 g sugar.

Salmon Chowder

15 servings

10 cups water
2 bouillon cubes
2 cups diced potatoes
2 tbsp. oil
1 cup diced onions
1 cup diced celery
2 cups diced carrots
1 tsp. sea salt
1 garlic clove, minced
1 tsp. dill weed
1 can creamed style corn
2 cups cooked salmon chunks or 2 cans of salmon, drained with bones and skin removed
1 can cocktail shrimp, drained

In a large soup pot, add the water and bouillon cubes and let simmer over medium-high heat.

Peel or scrub the potatoes and cut into bite-sized pieces. Place them in a medium-sized saucepan and cover with water. Place a lid on your pot, bring to a boil and then let the pot sit on low heat until the potatoes are cooked. Drain the water off of the potatoes and let cool.

In a large, non-stick frying pan, sauté the oil, onions, celery, and carrots until tender. Add to the soup pot. Then add the cooked potatoes, sea salt, garlic, and dill. Cover and simmer for 1 hour, stirring often.

Add the corn, salmon and shrimp. Heat through and let simmer for another hour, stirring often. Add water if the soup becomes too thick.

Per serving: 270 calories, 28 g protein, 19 carbohydrates, 8 g total fat, 1.9 g saturated fat, 3.54 g fiber, 1.2 g sodium, 4.5 g sugar.

Clam Chowder

10 servings

10 cups water
2 bouillon cubes
4 cups diced potatoes
4 bacon strips
2 cups diced carrots
2 cups sliced fresh mushrooms
2 cups diced onions
2 minced garlic cloves
1 tsp. dried parsley flakes
½ tsp. dill
1 tsp. pepper
1 bay leaf
1 large can baby clams
1 cup frozen peas
1 cup frozen corn
¼ cup flour
1 cup water

In a large soup pot, add the water and bouillon cubes and let simmer over medium-high heat.

Peel or scrub the potatoes and cut into bite-sized pieces. Place them in a medium-sized saucepan and cover with water. Place a lid on your pot, bring to a boil and then let the pot sit on low heat until the potatoes are cooked. Drain the water off of the potatoes and add them to the soup.

In a large, non-stick frying pan, cook the bacon slices until crisp. Remove and place on paper towels to drain. When cool, crumble and set aside.

In the same frying pan, sauté the carrots, mushrooms, onion and garlic in the bacon drippings until the carrots are tender. Add them to the soup pot along with the remaining spices. Bring to a boil, then turn the soup down to low and let simmer for one hour, stirring often.

Mix the flour with 1 cup water and stir until smooth, pour into the soup pot and stir until well mixed. Add the clams, frozen peas and corn and reduce the heat. Cover and simmer for one hour, stirring often. Remove the bay leaf. Garnish individual servings with bacon bits.

Per serving: 145 calories, 9 protein, 25 g carbohydrates, 1.3 g total fat, 0.3 g saturated fat, 4 g fiber, 545 mg sodium, 3.5 g sugar.

Chicken Rice Soup

8 servings

10 cups water
2 bouillon cubes
3 lbs. chicken thighs or breasts
2 cups diced onions
4 cups diced carrots
3 cups minced celery
1 cup uncooked brown rice
3 minced garlic cloves
2 tsp. oregano leaves
2 tbsp. dried parsley flakes
2 tsp. sea salt
Pepper to taste
2 cups frozen peas

In a large soup pot, add the water and bouillon cubes and let simmer over medium-high heat.

Brown the chicken in a hot frying pan, cutting the meat into bite-sized pieces as you go. When the chicken is done, add it to the soup pot. Then brown the vegetables (except the peas) in the frying pan with the chicken drippings until sizzling and mostly cooked through. Add the vegetables, the rice and the spices to the soup pot.

Bring the soup to a boil and then reduce the heat to low and let simmer for at least 2 − 3 hours, stirring often. Once an hour, bring the soup to just under a boil and then let simmer again afterwards. Keep adding water, one cup at a time, as the soup boils down. Add the frozen peas 15 minutes before serving.

Per serving: Calories 135, 7.8 g protein, 23 g carbohydrates, 1.2 g total fat, 0.3 g saturated fat, 5.3 g fiber, 0.9 g sodium, 4.9 g sugar.

Turkey Rice Soup

12 servings

10 cups turkey bone broth (made from boiling turkey bones)
1 bouillon cube
2 cups diced carrots
2 cups sliced fresh mushrooms
1 cup minced celery
2 cups diced onions
1 cup frozen peas
2 cups cubed cooked turkey
1 cup uncooked rice
2 bay leaves
2 minced garlic cloves
1 tsp. pepper
1 tsp. sea salt

In a large soup pot, heat up the turkey broth and let simmer on medium-high heat.

Add the remaining ingredients to the soup pot and bring to a boil. Reduce the heat, cover and simmer for at least three hours, stirring often. Add water if the soup becomes too thick, one cup at a time. Remove the bay leaves before serving.

Per serving: 160 calories, 19 g protein, 12 g carbohydrates, 3.3 g total fat, 0.7 g saturated fat, 3.3 g fiber, 520 mg sodium, 2 g sugar.

Country Vegetable Soup

10 servings

12 cups water
1 pkg. French onion soup mix
6 bacon strips
2 cups chopped zucchini
3 cups diced carrots
2 cups sliced celery
2 cups sliced mushrooms
1 cup diced onion
2 minced garlic cloves
1 cup frozen corn
1 bay leaf
½ tsp. dried basil
½ tsp. thyme
1 tsp. oregano leaves
1 tsp. pepper
3 cups uncooked noodles
1 cup frozen peas

In a large soup pot, add the water and the French onion soup mix. Let simmer over a medium-high heat.

In a large, non-stick frying pan, cook the bacon slices until crisp. Remove and place on paper towels to drain. When cool, crumble and set aside.

In the same frying pan, sauté the zucchini, carrots, celery, mushrooms, onion and garlic until the carrots are tender. Add these vegetables to the soup pot along with the frozen corn and remaining spices. Bring to a boil, then turn the soup down to low and let simmer for 2-3 hours, stirring often.

30 minutes before eating, cook the noodles in a separate saucepan. Drain and add to the soup pot, along with the frozen peas. Let simmer for 15 minutes, stirring frequently. Stir in the bacon bits and heat through.

Remove the bay leaf before serving.

Per serving: 118 calories, 5 g protein, 19 g carbohydrates, 3 g total fat, 1 g saturated fat, 3 g fiber, 205 mg sodium, 3 g sugar.

Beef Barley Soup

10 servings

10 cups water
2 bouillon cubes
1 lb. round steak, cut into tiny pieces
2 tbsp. oil, divided
½ cup medium pearl barley
1 tsp. oregano leaves
1 tsp. sea salt
1 tsp. pepper
3 tbsp. parsley flakes
3 cups diced carrots
2 cups minced celery
2 cups diced onion
2 minced garlic cloves
2 cups frozen peas

In a large soup pot, add the water and bouillon cubes and let simmer over medium-high heat.

In a large, non-stick frying pan, brown the steak cubes in 1 tbsp. oil and drain. Add the beef, the barley and the spices to the soup pot.

In the same frying pan, add 1 tbsp. oil and brown the carrots, celery, onion and garlic in the beef drippings until sizzling. Add the browned vegetables to the soup pot. Bring the soup to a boil. Reduce heat, cover and simmer for 2-3 hours, stirring often.

15 minutes before eating, add the frozen peas and heat through before serving.

Per serving: 150 calories, 13 g protein, 16g carbohydrates, 3.5 g total fat, 087 g saturated fat, 4.3 g fiber, 460 mg sodium, 3 g sugar.

Split Pea Soup

10 servings

10 cups water
2 bouillon cubes
2 cups dry split peas, rinsed
2 cups cubed ham
2 cups diced onions
2 cups shredded carrots
1 tbsp. oil
1 bay leaf
1 tsp. sea salt
1 tsp. pepper
½ tsp. dried rosemary, crushed
2 tbsp. dried parsley flakes

In a large soup pot, add the water and bouillon cubes and let simmer over medium-high heat.

Add the dried peas, bring to a boil, then reduce the heat to low, and let simmer.

In a large, non-stick frying pan, sauté the ham, onions and carrots in the oil until tender, then add them to the soup pot. Add the remaining ingredients to the soup, and bring to a boil. Reduce the heat, cover and simmer for 2-3 hours or until the peas are tender.

Add water if the soup becomes too thick, one cup at a time. Discard the bay leaves before serving.

Per serving: 170 calories, 11 g protein, 18 g carbohydrates, 5.6 g total fat, 1.4 g saturated fat, 5.7 g fiber, 1.3 g sodium, 3 g sugar.

STEWS

Meatball Stew

3 lbs. ground beef
1 tsp. garlic salt
1 tsp. Worcestershire sauce
2 tbsp. oil
4 cups beef broth
4 cups diced potatoes
4 cups diced carrots
2 cups diced onions
2 tbsp. parsley flakes
1 tsp. cumin
1 tsp. coriander
1 tsp. pepper

In a large mixing bowl, add the hamburger and sprinkle with the garlic salt and Worcestershire sauce. Mix well and shape into tiny, bite-sized meatballs. In a large, non-stick frying pan, brown the meatballs in the oil and drain.

Transfer the meatballs to a Dutch oven or covered roasting pan. Add the rest of the ingredients and mix well. Cover and bake at 350°F for 3 hours. Stir every 30 minutes and add water if needed.

Per serving: 340 calories, 18 g protein, 17 g carbohydrates, 22 g total fat, 8 g saturated fat, 3.4 g fiber, 480 mg sodium, 3 g sugar.

Hearty Beef Stew

12 servings

½ cup flour
4 lb. stewing beef
2-6 tbsp. oil
4 cups water
2 bouillon cubes
4 cups diced potatoes
4 cups diced carrots
2 cups diced onions
1 tsp. sea salt
1 tsp. pepper
2 minced garlic cloves

Place the flour in a large Ziploc bag. Add half of the stew beef and shake until the meat is coated with the flour. Repeat again with the second half of the stewing beef. Fry the flour-coated stew beef pieces in batches in a large, non-stick frying pan with 2 tbsp. oil in each batch. Turn the beef pieces until all sides are browned. Place the beef in the bottom of a Dutch oven or covered roasting pan. If you have no lid, cover the roasting pain securely with aluminum foil.

Boil the water in a kettle and mix with the bouillon cubes in a large measuring cup or bowl. Stir until the broth is made. Add the broth, potatoes, carrots, onions, sea salt, pepper and garlic to the stew beef. Stir well. Cover and bake at 350° for 2-3 hours. Check every 30 minutes and stir, adding water if necessary, one cup at a time. Let stand for 15 minutes uncovered before serving.

Per serving: 295 calories, 37 g protein, 19 g carbohydrates, 7.3 g total fat, 2.2 g saturated fat, 3 g fiber, 422 mg sodium, 2.5 g sugar.

Tender Pork Stew

16 servings

3 – 4 lbs. pork roast, trimmed and cut into inch cubes
1 tbsp. oil
4 cups water
2 bouillon cubes
1 cup diced onion
1 tsp. dried rosemary, crushed
1 tsp. oregano leaves
1 tsp. sea salt
1 tsp. pepper
4 cups cubed red potatoes
1 10-oz pkg. frozen cut green beans
5 cups diced carrots
1 tsp. Dijon mustard
½ cup flour
1 cup water

In a large, non-stick frying pan, brown the pork cubes in the oil over medium heat and drain. Place the pork cubes in the bottom of a Dutch oven or covered roasting pan. If you have no lid, cover the roasting pain securely with aluminum foil.

Boil the water in a kettle and mix with the bouillon cubes in a large measuring cup or bowl. Stir until the broth is made.

Add the bouillon and the rest of the ingredients over top of the pork cubes. Stir well. Cover and bake at 350° F for 2 hours. Stir every 30 minutes and add water if necessary, one cup at a time.

1 hour before supper, mix the flour and 1 cup water until smooth. Add to the stew and stir well. Continue to bake for one hour more. Let stand for 15 minutes uncovered before serving.

Per serving: 400 calories, 20 g protein, 16 g carbohydrates, 28.4 g total fat, 9.6 g saturated fat, 3.1 g fiber, 370 mg sodium, 3 g sugar.

76

Chicken Noodle Stew

8 servings

3 lbs. chicken thighs or breasts
3 cups sliced mushrooms
6 cups diced carrots
3 cups diced onions
5 cups water, divided
2 bouillon cubes
1 tsp. black pepper
2 tsp. parsley flakes
1 tsp. coriander
¼ cup cornstarch
3 cups frozen peas
Hot pasta or broad egg noodles

In a large, non-stick frying pan, brown the chicken pieces and place in a Dutch oven or covered roasting pan.

Add the vegetables to the drippings in the frying pan and heat until halfway cooked. Mix the cornstarch and 1 cup water in a measuring cup. Stir with a fork until smooth. Add the cornstarch mixture, 4 cups of water, bouillon cubes, and spices to the cooking vegetables and stir well. Heat until the sauce has thickened and is bubbling. Pour over top of the chicken pieces, cover and bake at 350° for 2-3 hours. Stir every 30 minutes and add water, if necessary.

When you are ready to eat, uncover the stew and mix in the frozen peas. Let stand for 10 minutes. The stew will have cooled, and the peas will have cooked perfectly.

Serve the stew in bowls over the hot pasta.

Per serving: 230 calories, 14 g protein, 40 g carbohydrates, 2 g total fat, 0.4 g saturated fat, 7 g fiber, 400 mg sodium, 8 g sugar.

Easy Roasted Chicken and Vegetables

12 servings

4 lbs. chicken thighs or breasts
5 cups diced potatoes
6 cups diced carrots
3 cups sliced mushrooms
2 cups diced onions
3 tbsp. oil
2 minced garlic cloves
1 tsp. oregano leaves
1 tsp. basil leaves
1 tsp. sea salt
1 tsp. pepper
2 cups chicken broth

Place the raw chicken pieces into the bottom of a Dutch oven or covered roasting pan. In a large mixing bowl, add the diced vegetables, oil, garlic, oregano, basil, sea salt and pepper. Toss well. Pour on top of the chicken. Add the chicken broth to the mixture. Cover and bake at 350° F for approximately 2 hours. Remove from the oven, stir well and continue to bake, uncovered, for another 30 minutes. Add water if the chicken mixture appears dry. Test the potatoes for doneness before serving.

Per serving: 280 calories, 35 g protein, 19 g carbohydrates, 3.7 g total fat, 0.6 g saturated fat, 4.0 g fiber, 505 mg sodium, 4.1 g sugar.

The Best Slow Cooked Roast Beef

16 servings4-5 lb. roast
2 tsp. bouillon granules
1 tsp. black pepper
2 tbsp. dried parsley flakes
1 cup water
¼ cup flour
½ cup red or white wine (or water)
Salt and pepper to taste

Place the roast in a slow cooker, and sprinkle with the bouillon granules, black pepper and parsley flakes. Pour the water in the bottom of the slow cooker. Cover and cook on high for 5 - 6 hours. When done, transfer the meat to another dish to carve.

Strain the juices to remove any browned bits, pour the beef juice into a medium saucepan and set to medium-high heat.

In a measuring cup, stir the flour and the wine (or water) with a fork until smooth. Pour the mixture into the beef drippings and continue to heat and stir until a gravy is formed. Add salt and pepper to taste.

Per serving: 430 calories, 30 g protein, 2 g carbohydrates, 25 g total fat, 2 g saturated fat, .01 g fiber, 324 mg sodium, 0 g sugar.

Slow-Cooked Beef Stew

12 servings

3 lbs. stewing beef, cubed
½ cup flour
3-6 tbsp. oil, divided
4 cups diced carrots
2 cups diced onions
2 cups sliced mushrooms
2 cups minced celery
1 cup water
1 cup beef broth
1 tsp. Dijon mustard
½ tsp. thyme
1 tsp. sea salt
1 tsp. black pepper
1 tsp. Worcestershire sauce
Cooked mashed potatoes OR cooked rice OR cooked noodles

In a large Ziploc plastic bag, add the flour and half of the stewing beef, seal and toss to coat evenly. (Repeat again with the 2nd half of the stewing beef.) In a large, non-stick frying pan, brown all sides of the meat in 2 tbsp. oil in batches. Pour into the bottom of your slow cooker. Layer the carrots, onions, mushrooms and celery on top.

In a measuring cup, combine the rest of the ingredients, stir until smooth and pour over the beef. Cover and cook on low for at least 8 hours or until the meat and vegetables are tender.

Just before serving, fry up your mashed potatoes, or cook rice or noodles. Serve the stew in bowls over your potatoes, rice or noodles.

Per serving: 463 calories, 35 g protein, 22 g carbohydrates, 26 g total fat, 2 g saturated fat, 4 g fiber, 410 mg sodium, 3 g sugar.

Slow-Cooked Turkey Stew

10 servings

3 lbs. ground turkey
2 cups sliced mushrooms
2 cups chopped carrots
1 cup chopped onions
2 minced garlic cloves
1 tsp. ground thyme
1 tsp. dried basil
1 tsp. pepper
1 tsp. sea salt
2 tsp. parsley flakes
¼ cup flour
1 cup white wine
2 cups boiling water
1 bouillon cube
1 tsp. Worcestershire sauce
Cooked mashed potatoes OR cooked rice OR cooked noodles

In your slow cooker, add the turkey, the chopped vegetables and the spices and stir well. Mix the flour, wine, boiling water, bouillon cube and Worcestershire sauce in a large measuring cup or bowl. Stir until smooth and pour over the turkey and vegetables. Cover and cook on low for approximately 8 hours. Just before serving, stir well, breaking up any large turkey cubes that have formed.

30 minutes before eating, fry up your mashed potatoes, or cook your rice or noodles. Serve the stew in bowls over your potatoes, rice or noodles.

Per serving: 305 calories, 29 g protein, 14 g carbohydrates, 13 g total fat, 3.4 g saturated fat, 2.4 g fiber, 440 mg sodium, 2 g sugar.

Slow-Cooked Teriyaki Sandwiches

8 servings

2 lbs. boneless chuck steak
¼ cup soya sauce
2 tbsp. brown sugar
1 tsp. ground ginger
2 minced garlic cloves
2 tbsp. cornstarch
¼ cup water
8 rolls, split
Pineapple rings
¼ cup toasted sesame seeds

Cut the steak into thin strips and place them in the bottom of your slow cooker. In a measuring cup, combine the soya sauce, brown sugar, ginger and garlic and pour the sauce over top of the meat. Cover and cook on low for 8 hours or until the meat is tender.

Remove the meat with a slotted spoon and set aside. Carefully pour the liquid into a large measuring cup. Add water to the liquid to measure 2 cups. Pour into a large saucepan. Combine the cornstarch and water until smooth and add to the pan. Cook and stir over medium-high heat until thick and bubbly, approximately 5 minutes. Add the meat and heat through.

Cut the rolls in half and broil them 4-5 inches from the heat until lightly toasted. Fill the rolls with meat and sauce, and then top with the pineapple rings and sesame seeds.

Note: to toast sesame seeds, please them in a non-stick frying pan over medium heat. Heat and stir until they are done to your liking.

Per serving: 255 calories, 22 g protein, 13 g carbohydrates, 13 g total fat, 3 g saturated fat, 0.4 g fiber, 290 mg sodium, 9 g sugar.

Slow-Cooked Oriental Chicken

8 servings

4 lbs. chicken thighs or breasts
1 cup diced onions
1 tbsp. oil
¼ cup soya sauce
2 tbsp. brown sugar
2 tbsp. water
1 garlic clove, minced
1 tsp. ground ginger
1 tbsp. cornstarch
¼ cup cold water
¼ cup slivered almonds

In a large, non-stick frying pan, over medium-high heat, brown the chicken in oil on both sides. Transfer to a slow cooker. In the same frying pan, cook the onions in the chicken drippings. When the onions are sizzling, combine the soya sauce, brown sugar, water, garlic and ginger, and pour it over the onions. Stir and heat until a sauce is formed and bubbling. Pour the onion mixture over the chicken pieces.

Set your slow cooker to low; cook 4 - 5 hours or until the meat juices run clear.

Remove the chicken to a serving platter and place in your oven at 300° F to keep warm. Transfer the drippings in the slow cooker to a saucepan. Mix 1 tbsp. cornstarch with ¼ cup water in a measuring cup and stir until smooth. Add it to the saucepan and drippings and heat over medium-high until thick and bubbling (approximately 5 minutes). Pour over the chicken pieces and garnish with almonds.

Per serving: 320 calories, 49 g protein, 10 g carbohydrates, 3.4 g total fat, 0.6 g saturated fat, 0.8 g fiber, 360 mg sodium, 5.5 g sugar.

Slow-Cooked Lemon Chicken

8 servings

3 lbs. chicken thighs or breasts
1 tsp. dried oregano leaves
½ tsp. sea salt
1 tsp. pepper
2 tbsp. oil
¼ cup water
¼ cup frozen lemonade concentrate
2 minced garlic cloves
1 tsp. bouillon granules
2 tbsp. cornstarch
¼ cup cold water
Hot cooked rice

Mix the oregano, sea salt and pepper together and rub over the chicken. In a large, non-stick frying pan over medium heat, brown the chicken in the oil and transfer to your slow cooker. Add the water, lemonade concentrate, garlic, and bouillon granules to the frying pan and bring to a boil, stirring to loosen any browned bits. Bring to bubbling and stir well. Pour over the chicken. Cover and cook on low heat for 5-6 hours or until the meat juices run clear.

Remove the chicken to a serving platter and place in your oven at 300° F to keep warm. Transfer the drippings in the slow cooker to a saucepan. Mix the cornstarch with ¼ cup water in a measuring cup and stir until smooth. Add it to the saucepan and drippings, and heat over medium-high until thick and bubbling (approximately 5 minutes). Pour over the chicken pieces, and serve with the hot rice.

Per serving: 350 calories, 38 g protein, 27 g carbohydrates, 4.4 g total fat, 0.7 g saturated fat, 2 g fiber, 340 mg sodium, 2 g sugar.

Slow-Cooked Cranberry Pork Roast

12 servings

3-5 lb. boneless rolled pork loin roast
2 tbsp. oil
1 can whole-berry cranberry sauce
¼ cup brown sugar
1 tsp. Dijon mustard
½ tsp. ginger
¼ cup cornstarch
¼ cup cold water
Sea salt to taste

In a large, non-stick frying pan, brown the pork roast in the oil on all sides over medium-high heat. Transfer to your slow cooker. Combine the cranberry sauce, brown sugar, mustard and ginger and pour over the roast. Cover and cook on low heat for 6-8 hours. Remove the roast and keep warm.

Pour the cranberry gravy into a medium saucepan and heat over medium-high. In a measuring cup, combine the cornstarch and cold water and stir until smooth. Add the cornstarch mixture to the saucepan, stirring constantly until thickened. Serve with the pork roast.

Per serving: 365 calories, 42 g protein, 26 g carbohydrates, 10 g total fat, 2.8 g saturated fat, 0.5 g fiber, 110 mg sodium, 23 g sugar.

Honey Dijon Chicken

10 servings

This recipe gets rave reviews every time I make it.
3 lbs. chicken thighs or breasts
½ cup liquid honey
¼ cup Dijon mustard
2 tsp. soya sauce
2 tsp. dried parsley flakes
6 cups hot rice or noodles

Place the raw chicken pieces in a 9 x 9 ovenproof baking dish that has been coated with non-stick cooking spray. In a measuring cup, mix the liquid honey, mustard and soya sauce. Pour the honey-mustard mixture over the chicken and sprinkle the parsley flakes over top. Bake at 350° F for approximately 60 minutes or until the chicken is cooked through.

Serve with hot rice or noodles.

Per serving: 205 calories, 29 g protein, 14 g carbohydrates, 0 g total fat, 0 g saturated fat, 0 g fiber, 220 mg sodium, 14 g sugar.

Fried Chicken Skillet

12 servings

4 lbs. chicken thighs or breasts
1 cup minced onions
3 cups diced carrots
2 cups minced celery
3 cups sliced mushrooms
8 cups cooked pasta
¼ cup oil
Salt and pepper

Heat a large, non-stick frying pan and brown the chicken pieces on both sides. When mostly cooked, cut the chicken into bite-sized pieces and continue to fry until completely cooked. Place in an ovenproof baking dish and sprinkle with salt and pepper. Keep warm in your oven at 250°F.

In the same frying pan, add your oil and vegetables and cook in the chicken drippings until sizzling. Then add your cooked pasta. Stir often to avoid burning. Add more oil if necessary. When the pasta and vegetables are close to being done, add the chicken back into the frying pan and cook for another 5 minutes.

Per serving: 370 calories, 39 g protein, 35 g carbohydrates, 4.4 g total fat, 0.7 g saturated fat, 3.3 g fiber, 330 mg sodium, 2.3 g sugar.

Baked Chicken Fingers

8 servings

Chicken Fingers

1 cup crushed cornflakes
½ cup flour
1 tsp. salt
1 tsp. black pepper
1 tsp. coriander
1 tsp. dried parsley flakes
1 tsp. garlic powder
3 lbs. chicken thighs or breasts
3 beaten eggs

Plum Sauce

You can use ready-made plum sauce, but this recipe is delicious!!

1 cup plum jam
2 tbsp. vinegar
2 tsp. Dijon mustard

In a medium bowl, combine the cornflakes, flour and spices. Mix well and set aside. Cut the chicken pieces lengthwise into strips. Place the strips into a medium-sized bowl. Beat the eggs with a fork and pour over the chicken. Mix with a spoon until coated.

Roll the chicken strips in the cornflake mixture, one at a time and place them on a baking sheet lined with parchment paper. Bake for 25 minutes at 350° F or until the chicken is cooked through.

Combine the plum jam, vinegar and Dijon mustard in a small saucepan. Cook on medium-high until bubbling, and serve warm with the chicken fingers.

Per serving: 355 calories, 39 g protein, 35 g carbohydrates, 1.9 g total fat, 0.6 g saturated fat, 0.3 g fiber, 490 mg sodium, 25 g sugar.

Honey-Glazed Chicken Wings

8 servings

3 lbs. chicken wings
½ cup liquid honey
¼ cup soya sauce
3 tbsp. oil
1 tsp. garlic powder
2 tsp. Worcestershire sauce
1 tsp. ground ginger

Place the chicken wing pieces into a marinating container (one with a lid that can be flipped without leaking) or a large Ziploc freezer bag. If you are using a freezer bag, we recommend doubling them up and making sure they are properly sealed.

In a large measuring cup, add the rest of the ingredients, stir well, and pour over the chicken wings. Seal the container or Ziploc bag and turn several times to coat. Refrigerate for at least 2 hours, but the wings are better if you can marinate them overnight, flipping the wings every time you open the fridge.

Drain and discard the marinade. Place parchment paper on the bottom of a large baking dish or 2 cookie sheets. If you don't have parchment paper, spray the pan with non-stick cooking spray.

Bake at 375° F on convection bake for 30 minutes, until the wings are cooked through.

Per serving: 155 calories, 3.1 g protein, 15 g carbohydrates, 5.1 g total fat, 1.3 g saturated fat, 0.1 g fiber, 472 mg sodium, 20 g sugar.

Tangy Pineapple Chicken

10 servings

3 lbs. chicken thighs or breasts
Sea salt and pepper to taste
1 tsp. dried basil
1 tbsp. oil
1 20-oz can unsweetened pineapple chunks
3 tbsp. Dijon mustard
¼ cup liquid honey
2 minced garlic cloves
1 tbsp. cornstarch
½ cup water
6 cups hot rice

Cook your rice according to instructions so that it will be hot and ready when your chicken is done.

Sprinkle the chicken with basil, salt and pepper. In a large, non-stick frying pan, brown the chicken in the oil. Drain the pineapple, reserving the juice. In a measuring cup, stir the cornstarch and 2 tbsp. pineapple juice until smooth, then set aside. Combine the mustard, liquid honey, garlic and remaining pineapple juice and mix well. Add to the frying pan with the chicken pieces and bring to a boil.

Reduce the heat, cover and simmer for 30 minutes longer. Remove the chicken and keep it warm. Add the cornstarch and pineapple mixture to the pan and bring to a boil, stirring constantly until thickened. Return the chicken to the pan, top with pineapple and heat through.

Serve over hot rice.

Per serving: 350 calories, 32 g protein, 42 g carbohydrates, 1.6 g total fat, 0.3 g saturated fat, 0.8 g fiber, 200 mg sodium, 14 g sugar.

Chicken Stir-Fry

10 servings

3 lbs. chicken thighs or breasts cut into strips
2 minced garlic cloves
1 tbsp. oil
½ cup apple juice
¼ cup soya sauce
2 cups diced carrots
2 cups diced celery
1 cup diced onions
1 tbsp. cornstarch
¼ cup cold water
2 cups bean sprouts
6 cups hot cooked rice

In a non-stick frying pan or wok, stir-fry the chicken strips, garlic, and oil until the chicken is cooked through. Combine the apple juice and soya sauce and add to the hot chicken and stir well. Set aside.

In the same pan, stir fry the carrots, celery and onions in the chicken drippings for 5 minutes. Add 2 tbsp. oil if necessary. Pour the chicken mixture back into the frying pan, and cook for another 5 minutes.

In a measuring cup, combine the cornstarch and cold water until smooth and gradually add it to the frying pan. Bring to a boil, cook and stir until thickened and bubbly. Add the bean sprouts at the last minute and stir until coated.

Serve over hot rice.

Per serving: 292 calories, 32 g protein, 28 g carbohydrates, 2.3 g total fat, 0.4 g saturated fat, 3.2 g fiber, 470 mg sodium, 4.5 g sugar.

Chicken with Lemon Sauce

3 lbs. chicken thighs or breasts
½ cup flour
1 tsp. sea salt
1 tsp. dried parsley flakes
3 extra-large eggs
2 tbsp. oil
1 bouillon cube
1 cup water
½ cup apple juice
1 tbsp. flour
¼ cup water
1 tbsp. lemon juice
1 tbsp. dried parsley flakes
6 cups hot noodles or rice

Place the chicken pieces between two pieces of waxed paper and pound with a rolling pin until they are ¼ inch thick. In a shallow bowl, combine the flour, sea salt and parsley flakes. In another bowl, beat the eggs. Dip the chicken in the egg mixture and then coat with the flour mixture.

Preheat a large, non-stick frying pan to medium-high, and then brown the chicken pieces in the oil for 5 minutes on each side, or until completely cooked through. Remove the chicken and place it in an ovenproof baking dish. Keep warm in the oven at 300° F.

Add the apple juice, bouillon cube and 1 cup of water to the frying pan and stir to loosen any browned bits. Mix the flour, ¼ cup of water and lemon juice in a measuring cup with a fork and stir until smooth. Add to the apple juice mixture and cook and stir until thickened and bubbly. Pour the sauce over the chicken and bake in the oven for 30 minutes, or until the chicken and sauce is hot and bubbling.

Serve with rice or noodles and garnish with parsley flakes.

Per serving: 220 calories, 30 g protein, 6.3 g carbohydrates, 3.7 g total fat, 0.7 g saturated fat, 0.2 g fiber, 425 mg sodium, 1.3 g sugar.

Chicken in Pear Sauce

10 servings

5 thick cut bacon strips
3 lbs. chicken thighs or breasts
3 cups water
1 bouillon cube
½ cup diced onions
3 medium ripe pears, peeled and diced
2 tbsp. cornstarch
¼ cup cold water
6 cups hot, cooked rice or noodles

In a large, non-stick frying pan, cook the bacon until crisp. Drain and set the bacon aside. Crumble when cool.

In the same frying pan over medium heat, cook the chicken in the bacon drippings for about 10 minutes on each side or until the juices run clear. Remove the chicken pieces and place them in an ovenproof dish to keep warm in the oven at 300° F.

Add the water, the bouillon and the onions into the frying pan, scraping the pan to loosen any browned bits and bring to a boil. Add the pears and let simmer for 10 minutes or until tender.

In a measuring cup, combine the cornstarch and water until smooth. Gradually stir the cornstarch mixture into the pear mixture, sprinkle the bacon on top and cook until thickened and bubbly.

Add the chicken back into the frying pan, stir well to coat and let bubble away for another 5 minutes, stirring often.

Serve over hot rice or noodles.

Per serving: 200 calories, 30 g protein, 8 g carbohydrates, 1.6 g total fat, 0.5 g saturated fat, 1.4 g fiber, 260 mg sodium, 4.2 g sugar.

Apple Walnut Chicken

3 lbs. chicken thighs or breasts
2 cups diced apples
½ cup chopped walnuts
2 tbsp. cornstarch
2 cups apple juice
1 tbsp. vinegar
2 tsp. Dijon mustard
1 tsp. ginger
Hot rice or noodles

Place the raw chicken pieces in a large baking dish coated with non-stick cooking spray. Sprinkle the apples and walnuts over top of the chicken. In a large measuring cup, stir together the cornstarch, apple juice, vinegar, Dijon mustard and ginger. Pour over top of the chicken. Cover and bake for one hour at 350° F or until the chicken juices run clear.

Serve over rice or noodles.

Per serving: 250 calories, 26 g protein, 20 g carbohydrates, 4.0 g total fat, 0.5 g saturated fat, 2.0 g fiber, 93 mg sodium, 2.1 g sugar.

Marinated Garlic Chicken BBQ

12 servings

4 lbs. chicken thighs or breasts
½ cup oil
3 cloves garlic
2 cups apple juice
2 diced green onions
1 tsp. parsley flakes
1 tsp. coriander

Place the chicken pieces in a marinating container (one with a lid that can be flipped without leaking) or a large Ziploc freezer bag. If you are using a freezer bag, we recommend doubling them up and making sure they are properly sealed.

Mix the other ingredients together in a large measuring cup and pour over the chicken pieces. Let stand for 8 hours or overnight, flipping the chicken every time you open your fridge.

Discard the marinade and BBQ when ready, making sure that the chicken is thoroughly cooked before serving.

Per serving: 266 calories, 32 g protein, 5.2 g carbohydrates, 9.1 g total fat, 1.2 g saturated fat, 0.3 g fiber, 98 mg sodium, 4 g sugar.

Turkey Meatballs

8 servings

2 lbs. lean ground turkey or chicken
½ cup minced onion
1 tsp. parsley flakes
1 tsp. oregano leaves
2 minced garlic cloves
½ tsp. sea salt
1 tsp. pepper
2 tbsp. oil
1 cup plum jam
1 tsp. vinegar
2 tbsp. Dijon mustard
6 cups hot, cooked rice or noodles

Combine the ground turkey or chicken, onions, parsley flakes, oregano, garlic, sea salt and pepper in a medium bowl. Mix well. Form the mixture into bite size meatballs. Cook the meatballs in a large, non-stick frying pan in the oil and transfer to an ovenproof baking dish when done.

In a small saucepan, add the jam, vinegar and Dijon mustard. Cook, stirring often over medium heat, until the sauce is thick and bubbly. Pour the sauce over the meatballs, then bake uncovered for 30 minutes at 325° F.

Serve over hot rice or noodles.

Per serving: 347 calories, 24 g protein, 43 g carbohydrates, 8.2 g total fat, 2.6 g saturated fat, 0.6 g fiber, 330 mg sodium, 18 g sugar.

Turkey Stir-Fry

10 servings

2 lbs. raw boneless turkey breast, cut into strips
OR ground turkey
2 tbsp. oil
2 cups diced carrots
2 cups fresh zucchini, cut into bite-sized pieces
3 cups sliced fresh mushrooms
1 cup diced onions
2 minced garlic cloves
½ tsp. ground ginger
½ cup water
2 tbsp. soya sauce
2 tsp. cornstarch
1 8-oz can sliced water chestnuts, drained
4 cups hot cooked white or brown rice

In a large, non-stick frying pan or wok, stir fry the turkey in the oil over medium-high heat until cooked through. Remove and keep warm. Stir-fry the carrots, garlic and ginger in the turkey drippings for 5 minutes, adding 2 tbsp. of oil if necessary. Then add the zucchini, mushrooms, and onions and cook for another 5 minutes until the vegetables are crisp-tender.

In a measuring cup, combine the cornstarch, soya sauce and water and add it to the vegetables along with the water chestnuts. Cook and stir until thickened. Add the turkey to the hot vegetables and stir fry for another 3-5 minutes.

Serve over hot rice.

Per serving: 285 calories, 21 g protein, 28 g carbohydrates, 9.7 g total fat, 2.5 g saturated fat, 3.5 g fiber, 210 mg sodium, 3 g sugar.

SEAFOOD

Marinated BBQ Salmon

10 servings

We have to buy extra salmon when we serve this recipe. Everyone wants seconds!

4 lbs. salmon fillets, cut it into individual servings
1 cup soya sauce
2 tbsp. brown sugar
1 tbsp. dry mustard

Place the salmon fillets in a marinating container (one with a lid that can be flipped without leaking) or a large Ziploc freezer bag. If you are using a freezer bag, we recommend doubling them up and making sure they are properly sealed.

Mix the remaining ingredients and reserve 1/3 cup for later. Pour the remaining liquid over the salmon fillets and marinate for at least 2 hours.

BBQ over a medium-high heat, 5 minutes a side. It is important to time yourself when barbequing salmon as it can overcook easily. Use the reserved marinade to brush on your salmon while cooking.

Per serving: 360 calories, 37 g protein, 6 g carbohydrates, 20 g total fat, 0 g saturated fat, 0 g fiber, 400 mg sodium, 6 g sugar.

Maple Teriyaki Salmon Fillets

8 servings

½ cup apple juice
½ cup maple syrup
¼ cup soya sauce
½ cup minced onion
2 minced garlic cloves
3 lbs. salmon fillets

In a bowl, combine everything except the salmon. Remove ½ cup for basting; cover and refrigerate. Place the salmon in a marinating container (one with a lid that can be flipped without leaking) or a large Ziploc freezer bag. If you are using a freezer bag, we recommend doubling them up and making sure they are properly sealed.

Pour the remaining marinade over top. Refrigerate for at least 3 hours, flipping the salmon every 30 minutes or so.

Drain and discard the marinade. BBQ over medium-high heat, 5 minutes a side (time this!!) or broil the salmon 4 inches from the heat for 10 minutes a side. Baste with the reserved marinade.

Per serving: 280 calories, 24 g protein, 18 g carbohydrates, 13 g total fat, 0 g saturated fat, 0.2 g fiber, 430 mg sodium, 15 g sugar.

Classic Crab Cakes

8 servings

2 cups canned or cooked crabmeat, flaked with the cartilage removed
2 cups soft breadcrumbs, crumbled
3 beaten eggs
1 cup mayonnaise or Miracle Whip
½ cup minced celery
¼ cup minced green onion
1 tsp. dried parsley flakes
2 tsp. lemon juice
1 tsp. Worcestershire sauce
1 tsp. Dijon mustard
½ tsp. pepper
2 to 4 tbsp. oil
Lemon slices

In a bowl, combine all of the ingredients except the oil and the lemon slices. Shape into 8 patties. In a large, non-stick frying pan, cook the patties in the oil until golden brown. Serve with lemon slices.

Per serving: 410 calories, 13 g protein, 20 g carbohydrates, 30 g total fat, 5 g saturated fat, 1.5 g fiber, 500 mg sodium, 2 g sugar.

Oven Baked Fish 'n' Chips

8 servings

Chips

8 medium baking potatoes, scrubbed or peeled
¼ cup oil
½ tsp. sea salt
½ tsp. black pepper
1 tsp. dried parsley flakes
4 minced garlic cloves with a garlic press

Fish

½ cup flour
¼ tsp. sea salt
¼ tsp. pepper
3 eggs
1 cup crushed cornflakes
2 lb. frozen cod or halibut fillets, thawed

Cut your potatoes lengthwise into thin wedges and place in a large mixing bowl. Pour the oil over the potatoes, add the salt, pepper, parsley flakes and garlic and toss to coat. Place on 2 baking sheets lined with parchment paper and bake covered with aluminum foil at 425° F for 20 minutes. Turn the potato wedges and bake for another 20 minutes or until golden brown and crisp.

Meanwhile, prepare the fish. Combine the flour, sea salt and pepper in a shallow dish. In a second dish, beat the eggs. In a third dish, add the crushed cornflakes. Coat the fish in the flour, dip it in the egg mixture and then roll it in the cornflakes.

Place the fish on a cookie sheet lined with parchment paper. Bake at 425° F for 15-20 minutes or until the fish flakes easily with a fork.

Per serving: 375 calories, 23 g protein, 50 g carbohydrates, 10 g total fat, 1.4 g saturated fat, 4.3 g fiber, 330 mg sodium, 3 g sugar.

Honey-Glazed Ham

12 servings

3-5 lb. ham – bone in or bone out
½ cup water
½ cup liquid honey
¼ cup Dijon mustard
2 tbsp. soya sauce

Score the ham, making diamond shapes ½ inches deep. Place on a rack in a Dutch oven or covered roasting pan. In a small bowl, combine the rest of the ingredients and pour over the ham. Bake, covered at 350° F for 2 hours or until the ham is cooked through. Baste with pan juices every 30 minutes. If you like your ham more browned, take the cover off for the last 30 minutes.

Per serving: 318 calories, 35 g protein, 12 g carbohydrates, 14 g total fat, 4.7 g saturated fat, 0.1 g fiber, 1 g sodium, 12 g sugar.

Apricot Pork Chops

6 servings

6 pork chops
1 cup minced onions
1 cup diced celery
½ cup apricot jam
½ cup raisins
1 tsp. ground ginger
½ tsp. sea salt
½ cup toasted, slivered almonds
6 cups hot, cooked rice

In a large, non-stick frying pan over medium heat, brown the pork chops for 5 minutes on each side, remove and place in a large baking pan. In the same frying pan, sauté the onions and celery in the pork drippings until tender. Add the apricot jam, raisins, ginger, and sea salt and bring to a boil, stirring constantly.

Pour the sauce over the pork chops. Cover and bake at 350° F for 45 minutes or until the pork is cooked through.

Serve over hot rice and garnish with the toasted almonds.

Note: to toast the slivered almonds, place them in a small non-stick frying pan over medium heat. Stir until they become toasty brown.

Per serving: 500 calories, 35 g protein, 40 g carbohydrates, 15 g total fat, 4.5 g saturated fat, 3 g fiber, 288 mg sodium, 17 g sugar.

Grilled Pork Chops

6 servings

6 pork chops (about 1 inch thick)
1 cup diced onions
½ cup water
½ cup soya sauce
½ cup packed brown sugar
¼ cup lime juice
1 garlic clove, minced

Place the pork chops in a marinating container (one with a lid that can be flipped without leaking) or a large Ziploc freezer bag. If you are using a freezer bag, we recommend doubling them up and making sure they are properly sealed.

Combine the remaining ingredients and set aside 1/3 cup for basting. Pour the remaining marinade over the pork, and refrigerate for several hours or overnight, turning frequently. Drain and discard the marinade.

Grill or BBQ the pork chops over medium heat until thoroughly cooked. Baste with reserved marinade.

Per serving: 345 calories, 33 g protein, 30 g carbohydrates, 12 g total fat, 4 g saturated fat, 0.5 g fiber, 650 mg sodium, 25 g sugar.

Lemon Apple Pork Chops

6 servings

6 pork chops
1 tbsp. oil
1 cup apple juice
¼ cup lemon juice
1 tsp. oregano leaves
½ tsp. sea salt
½ tsp. black pepper
1 cup diced onions
1 large apple peeled and diced into bite-sized pieces
1 tsp. cornstarch
¼ cup cold water
6 cups hot, cooked rice

In a large, non-stick frying pan, over medium-high heat, brown the pork chops in the oil. Remove the pork chops and place in an ovenproof baking dish.

In the same frying pan, add the apple juice, lemon juice, oregano, sea salt and pepper and cook in the pork drippings. Stir well, loosening any brown bits. Add the onions and apple pieces and continue to cook. In a measuring cup, combine the cornstarch and ¼ cup cold water until smooth and gradually into the pan. Continue to cook for another 5 minutes, or until thickened.

Pour the sauce over the pork chops and bake, covered at 350° F for one hour or until the pork juices run clear.

Serve over the hot rice.

Per serving: 400 calories, 35 g protein, 30 g carbohydrates, 15 g total fat, 4.5 g saturated fat, 3 g fiber, 110 mg sodium, 7 g sugar.

Plum Glazed Pork Chops

6 servings

6 bone-in pork chops
2 tsp. cornstarch
½ tsp. ground ginger
2 tbsp. soya sauce
¼ cup water
½ cup plum jam
2 tbsp. freshly squeezed lime juice
2 minced garlic cloves
1 small lime, thinly sliced
6 cups hot rice or noodles

In a large, non-stick frying pan, brown the pork chops on both sides over medium-high heat and transfer to a baking dish.

In a large measuring cup, combine the cornstarch, ginger, soya sauce and water. Pour into the frying pan. Heat and stir until smooth, loosening up any browned bits. Then add the plum jam, lime juice and garlic and continue to cook and stir until well blended. Bring to a boil, cook and stir for 5 minutes or until thickened.

Pour the sauce over the pork chops and bake, covered at 350° F for one hour or until the pork juices run clear.

Serve over hot rice or noodles. Garnish with lime slices.

Per serving: 285 calories, 20 g protein, 20 g carbohydrates, 13 g total fat, 4.6 g saturated fat, 0.1 g fiber, 240 mg sodium, 17 g sugar.

Mustard-Glazed Pork Chops

6 servings

6 bone-in pork loin chops
2 tbsp. oil
½ cup apple or pineapple juice
½ cup packed brown sugar
¼ cup Dijon mustard
¼ cup cider vinegar
Dried parsley flakes

In a large, non-stick frying pan, brown the pork chops on both sides over medium-high heat and transfer to a baking dish coated with non-stick cooking spray.

In the same frying pan, add the apple or pineapple juice, brown sugar, Dijon mustard and cider vinegar and cook along with the pork drippings. Continue to cook, stirring frequently. Reduce the heat, cover and simmer for 5 minutes or until thickened.

Pour the sauce over top of the pork chops and sprinkle the parsley flakes over top. Bake, uncovered, at 350° F for 45 minutes or until the juices run clear.

Per serving: 300 calories, 20 g protein, 30 g carbohydrates, 13 g total fat, 4.6 g saturated fat, 0 g fiber, 230 mg sodium, 27 g sugar.

Maple Country Ribs

12 servings

3 lbs. country-style pork ribs, cut into individual portions
½ cup maple syrup
½ cup applesauce
¼ cup lemon juice
1 tsp. sea salt
1 tsp. garlic powder

Line 3 cookie sheets with parchment paper. Place the ribs evenly over the 3 cookie sheets. Cover with tin foil and bake at 350° F convection bake for one hour.

In a large measuring cup, combine the remaining ingredients. Stir until smooth and keep until needed.

To make clean up easier on yourself, take 3 clean cookie sheets and line them with parchment paper (again!). If you have metal cooling racks, set them inside the cookie sheets. Place your cooked ribs evenly on these new cookie sheets and brush the sauce onto the ribs.

Reduce the heat on your oven to 275° F. Set your timer for 20 minute intervals, flip the ribs, and baste with the sauce. Continue in 20 minute intervals, for the next 60 minutes, or until the ribs are done to your liking.

Note – to clean your cookie sheets, wait until the drippings cool. Then peel off the grease saturated parchment paper and throw it away. You then have less mess to wash up.

Per serving: 500 calories, 28 g protein, 22 g carbohydrates, 30 g total fat, 13 g saturated fat, 0.4 g fiber, 320 mg sodium, 19 g sugar.

Pork Vegetable Stir-Fry

8 servings

2 lb. boneless pork, cut into thin strips
2 tbsp. oil
2 medium carrots, julienned
2 cups sliced mushrooms
2 minced garlic cloves
1 tsp. ground ginger
2 minced green onions
1 can whole baby corn, drained
1 cup snow peas
¼ cup cornstarch
1½ cup cold water, divided
¼ cup soya sauce
2 tbsp. liquid honey
2 tsp. chicken bouillon granules
6 cups hot cooked rice

In a large, non-stick frying pan or wok, over medium-high heat, stir-fry the pork strips in the oil, for 5 minutes. Add the carrots, mushrooms, garlic and ginger, and cook for another 5 minutes. Then add the green onions, corn and snow peas; continue to stir-fry until the vegetables are crisp-tender and the pork is no longer pink. Remove the meat and vegetables and keep them warm in your oven at 300°F.

In a large measuring cup, combine the cornstarch and ½ cup cold water and stir until smooth. In the same measuring cup, add the remaining water, soya sauce, liquid honey, and bouillon granules and mix well. Pour into the frying pan and continue to cook, stirring often, until the sauce is thickened. Add the meat and vegetables and toss, cook for another 3-5 minutes until everything is hot and bubbling. Serve over hot rice.

Per serving: 393 calories, 25 g protein, 40 g carbohydrates, 10 g total fat, 3 g saturated fat, 4.7 g fiber, 690 mg sodium, 8.2 g sugar.

Ginger-Spiced Pork Casserole

2 lbs. cubed pork roast
2 tbsp. oil
2 cups apple juice
2 cups water, divided
1 cup diced, peeled apple
½ cup dried cranberries
½ cup raisins
1 tsp. ground ginger
½ tsp. cloves
¼ cup flour
2 medium sweet potatoes, baked and cubed

In a large, non-stick frying pan, cook the pork cubes in the oil until no longer pink. Add the apple juice and 1 cup water and bring to a boil. Reduce the heat and simmer for 10 minutes. Stir in the fruit and spices and simmer 15 minutes longer. Mix the flour and 1 cup water and until smooth, then add to the meat mixture. Bring to a boil and cook for 5 minutes or until thickened. Stir in the sweet potatoes and pour everything into a large, greased baking dish. Bake at 400° F for 30 minutes or until heated through.

Per serving: 575 calories, 33 protein, 29 g carbohydrates, 35 g total fat, 12 g saturated fat, 2.2 g fiber, 100 mg sodium, 17 g sugar.

Sausage Shish Kebobs

6 servings

2 lb. fresh, cleaned whole mushrooms
4-6 small zucchinis, sliced into 1 inch pieces
1 large can pineapple chunks, drained
4-6 kielbasa sausages or smokies, cut into 1 inch pieces
¼ cup oil
2 minced garlic cloves

Soak wooden skewers in water for at least one hour. In a measuring cup, mix the oil and garlic and let sit for 30 minutes to marinate. Using a skewer, thread on the sausages, mushrooms, zucchini, and pineapple pieces in an alternating pattern. Place the shish kebobs on cookie sheets and brush them with the oil. Let sit for another 30 minutes.

Preheat your BBQ to medium low heat, and place on the grill. Cook for 5-7 minutes on each side, testing the zucchini and sausages for doneness. Baste with oil if necessary.

Per serving: 187 calories, 5.7 g protein, 14 g carbohydrates, 13 g total fat, 3.4 g saturated fat, 3.1 g fiber, 180 mg sodium, 8.7 g sugar.

BEEF

Hamburger Bake

10 servings

3 lbs. hamburger
6 potatoes, scrubbed or peeled and chopped
6 carrots, scrubbed or peeled and chopped
4 cups water
2 bouillon cubes
1 cup diced onion
2 cups sliced mushrooms
1 tsp. black pepper
1 tsp. coriander

In a large, non-stick frying pan, over medium-high heat, brown the hamburger, breaking it up into small pieces as you go. Drain and add to a large baking dish or roasting pan. Cover with the potatoes, carrots and mushrooms.

In the same frying pan, add the water, bouillon cubes, black pepper and coriander and heat through until the bouillon is dissolved and the liquid is bubbling. Pour over top of the cooked hamburger and vegetables and stir well.

Cover and bake at 350° for 3 hours, stirring every 30 minutes and checking that that pan hasn't gone dry. Add water if necessary, one cup at a time.

Per serving: 320 calories, 30 g protein, 24 g carbohydrates, 11 g total fat, 5 g saturated fat, 5 g fiber, 280 mg sodium, 5 g sugar.

Marinated Beef Wraps

(This is a 2 day recipe)

8 servings2 lb. flank steak
2 minced garlic cloves
¼ cup lime juice
¼ cup oil
2 minced green onions
2 tsp. Worcestershire sauce
½ tsp. sea salt
½ tsp. black pepper
2 cups sliced fresh mushrooms
1 cup onion, minced
2 tbsp. oil
2 tsp. cornstarch
¼ cup cold water
Lettuce leaves
8 Greek style pitas

Day 1

Cut the flank steak in thin slices across the grain. Place them in a marinating container (one with a lid that can be flipped without leaking) or a large Ziploc freezer bag. If you are using a freezer bag, we recommend doubling them up and making sure they are properly sealed.

In a large measuring cup, combine the minced garlic, lime juice, oil, green onions, Worcestershire sauce, sea salt and pepper. Mix well, and reserve ¼ cup of the marinade. (Cover and place in your fridge.) Pour the remaining marinade over the steak strips. Continue to marinade the steak strips overnight, flipping the container every time you go into the fridge.

Day 2

Drain the beef strips and discard the marinade.

In a large, non-stick frying pan, over medium-high heat, sauté the beef strips, onions and mushrooms in the 2 tbsp. oil until cooked through.

In a measuring cup, mix the cornstarch and cold water and stir with a fork until smooth. Add the reserved marinade to the cornstarch mixture and stir again. Pour over the beef strips and continue to cook and stir until the sauce has thickened.

Wrap up the Greek pitas in a big piece of tinfoil and place in your oven at 250° F for 30 minutes, or heat the pitas in the microwave so that they are easier to work with. Lay each warmed Greek pita flat, add a portion of the steak strip mixture in the middle and top with lettuce leaves. Roll up each pita with waxed paper to keep its shape before serving.

Per serving: 342 calories, 29 g protein, 32 g carbohydrates, 12 g total fat, 4 g saturated fat, 4.4 g fiber, 500 mg sodium, 0.8 g sugar.

Roast Beef Hash

6 servings

1 cup diced onions
3 tbsp. oil
3 cups frozen hash browned potatoes
3 cups minced, cooked roast beef
1 cup beef gravy
1 tsp. Worcestershire sauce
1 tsp. Dijon mustard
Salt to taste

In a large, non-stick frying pan, sauté the onions in the oil until tender. Stir in the hash browned potatoes and cook until the potatoes are hot and sizzling. Add the roast beef, gravy, mustard and Worcestershire sauce, and stir until well combined. Cook over medium heat, stirring occasionally until heated through and bubbling.

Per serving: 425 calories, 25 g protein, 20 g carbohydrates, 27 g total fat, 6 g saturated fat, 0.6 g fiber, 600 mg sodium, 0.2 g sugar.

Asian Pot Roast

16 servings

4-5 lb. chuck roast
2 tbsp. flour
1 tsp. garlic powder
1 tsp. sea salt
1 tsp. pepper
2 tbsp. oil
1 cup diced onions
2 cups water
1 cup plum jam
¼ cup cider vinegar
1 tsp. Dijon mustard
Cooked rice noodles

Combine the flour, garlic powder, sea salt and pepper and rub over the roast. In a large, non-stick frying pan, brown the roast in the oil. Remove to a large roasting pan. In the frying pan with the drippings, add the onions and water and cook for 5 minutes. Pour the onion mixture over the pot roast.

Cover the roasting pan and bake at 350° for 2 hours. Add extra water if necessary to keep the pan from burning on the bottom.

Slice the roast, then place it back into the roasting pan. Combine the plum jam, cider vinegar, and Dijon mustard and pour over the sliced roast. Stir well. Cover and simmer for one hour longer or until the meat is done to your liking.

Serve with hot rice noodles.

Per serving: 544 calories, 38 g protein, 35 g carbohydrates, 25 g total fat, 2.1 g saturated fat, 2 g fiber, 370 mg sodium, 2 g sugar.

Shepherd's Pie

10 servings

6 large potatoes
3 cups chicken broth, divided
3 lbs. ground beef
1 cup diced onions
3 cups sliced fresh mushrooms
3 large diced carrots
1 cup diced celery
1 tbsp. Worcestershire sauce
1 tsp. pepper
½ tsp. oregano leaves
½ tsp. basil
1 tsp. parsley flakes

Peel, chop and cook 6 large potatoes. Make into mashed potatoes using 1 cup of chicken broth instead of milk or margarine.

In a large, non-stick frying pan, cook the ground beef thoroughly. Drain off the excess fat, and place the hamburger in the bottom of a large baking dish.

In the same frying pan, cook the onions, mushrooms, carrots and celery in the hamburger drippings. Add the rest of the broth, Worcestershire sauce, oregano, basil and pepper. Bring to a boil and cook for 15 – 20 minutes or until tender. Pour over top of the hamburger. Stir the meat and vegetables together.

Spread the hot mashed potatoes evenly over top of everything else. Sprinkle with parsley flakes for color. Bake uncovered at 350° F for 30 minutes or until heated through.

Per serving: 490 calories, 29 g protein, 29 g carbohydrates, 29 g total fat, 11 g saturated fat, 4 g fiber, 380 mg sodium, 4 g sugar.

Ginger Beef Stir-Fry

8 servings

1 tbsp. cornstarch
1 tsp. liquid honey
½ tsp. ground ginger
2 lb. flank steak cut into thin strips
1 cup diced onions
1 tbsp. oil
¼ cup teriyaki sauce
2 medium carrots, thinly sliced
1 medium zucchini, thinly sliced
1 cups snow peas
6 cups hot cooked rice

In a medium bowl, whisk the cornstarch, liquid honey and ginger until smooth. Add the beef strips, toss to coat, and then set aside.

In a large, non-stick frying pan, sauté the onions in the oil for 3-5 minutes. Add the beef strips and stir-fry for 5-10 minutes or until the beef is cooked through. Stir in the teriyaki sauce. Add the carrots, zucchini and snow peas; stir-fry for 5 minutes or until the vegetables are crisp-tender.

Serve over hot rice.

Per serving: 390 calories, 28 g protein, 40 g carbohydrates, 12 g total fat, 4.2 g saturated fat, 4.6 g fiber, 250 mg sodium, 4.2 g sugar.

EGGS

Southern Hash

6 servings

4 cups frozen cubed hash brown potatoes; or cold, leftover diced
potatoes
½ cup diced onions
1 garlic clove, minced
3 tbsp. oil
3 cups cubed ham
6 eggs

In a large, non-stick frying pan, fry the potatoes, onion and garlic in the
oil until the potatoes are cooked through. Add the cubed ham and
continue to cook and stir for 5-10 minutes. Make six holes in the hash
browns and crack the eggs into the holes. Let stand until the eggs are
cooked to your liking and serve warm.

Per serving: 330 calories, 17 g protein, 24 g carbohydrates, 19 g total fat, 8 g saturated fat, 0.3 g
fiber, 750 mg sodium, 1 g sugar.

Potato Omelette Hash

4 servings

4 strips bacon
2 medium leftover cooked potatoes, diced
½ cup diced onions
2 minced garlic cloves
6 eggs
¼ cup water
½ tsp. sea salt

In a large, non-stick frying pan, cook the bacon strips until crisp. When done, set aside. Crumble when cool.

In the same frying pan, over medium-high heat, fry the potatoes, onions, and garlic in the bacon drippings for 10 minutes or until golden brown, stirring occasionally. Reduce the heat to medium.

In a mixing bowl beat the eggs, water and sea salt. Pour over the potato mixture and mix well; cover and cook for 10 minutes or until completely set. Cut into wedges. Garnish with the crumbled bacon.

Per serving: 240 calories, 16 g protein, 21 g carbohydrates, 11 g total fat, 3.5 g saturated fat, 2.3 g fiber, 290 mg sodium, 2 g sugar.

Mushroom Sausage Scramble

4 servings

1 lb. bulk pork sausage
1 cup diced onions
2 cups sliced fresh mushrooms
8 eggs
1 tsp. parsley flakes
¼ tsp. sea salt
Dash pepper

In a large, non-stick frying pan, cook the sausage, onions and mushrooms over medium-high heat. Stir often, breaking the sausage into small pieces until completely cooked.

In a bowl, whisk together the eggs, parsley flakes, sea salt and pepper. Pour over the sausage mixture and continue to stir and cook until the eggs are done.

Per serving: 320 calories, 15 g protein, 4 g carbohydrates, 17 g total fat, 10 g saturated fat, 0.8 g fiber, 750 mg sodium, 0.6 g sugar.

Breakfast Burritos

6 servings

½ cup minced onions
1 cup sliced fresh mushrooms
2 minced garlic cloves
2 tbsp. oil
1 cup cubed ham
6 eggs, well beaten
Sea salt
Pepper
6 soft flour or corn tortillas – avoid cheese, vegetable or sun dried tomato flavored tortillas

In a large, non-stick frying pan, sauté the onions, mushrooms, and garlic in the oil until browned and tender. Add the ham and heat through. Add the eggs to the mixture and let set, lifting the edges to let the uncooked egg flow underneath. When the eggs are set, flip to the other side to ensure that the eggs are cooked through.

Heat the tortillas in the microwave until warm, then add a few spoonfuls of egg mixture and sprinkle with sea salt and pepper to taste. Wrap the burrito up tightly.

Serve with the guacamole dip from our Snack section.

Per serving: 260 calories, 12 g protein, 23 g carbohydrates, 12 g total fat, 3.2 g saturated fat, 2.1 g fiber, 480 mg sodium, 2 g sugar.

Garlic Zucchini Frittata

4 servings

4 bacon strips
½ cup diced onion
2 minced garlic cloves
2 cups grated zucchini
1 cup grated carrots
6 eggs
1 tsp. Dijon mustard
¼ tsp. sea salt
Dash pepper

In a large, non-stick frying pan, cook the bacon slices until crisp. Remove and place on paper towels to drain. When cool, crumble and set aside.

In the same frying pan, sauté the onions and garlic in the bacon drippings for 3-5 minutes. Add the zucchini and carrots and cook for 5 minutes or until tender. Pour into a greased baking dish.

In a bowl, beat the eggs and mustard and pour over top of the vegetables. Sprinkle with the bacon, salt and pepper. Bake at 350° F uncovered for approximately 30 minutes or until eggs are done.

Cut into wedges or squares.

Per serving: 210 calories, 14 g protein, 6.5 g carbohydrates, 14 g total fat, 4 g saturated fat, 2 g fiber, 302 mg sodium, 1.8 g sugar.

Mushroom Wild Rice

8 servings

4½ cups water
1 cup uncooked wild rice
2 bouillon cubes
½ cup uncooked brown rice
2 cups sliced fresh mushrooms
1 cup diced onions
1 minced celery
2 tsp. oil
2 cups water
2 tbsp. cornstarch
¼ cup cold water
½ cup slivered almonds

In a large saucepan, add 4½ cups water, the wild rice and bouillon cubes, and bring to a boil. Reduce the heat, cover and let simmer for 40 minutes. Stir in the brown rice. Cover and simmer 40 minutes longer or until the rice is tender.

In a large, non-stick frying pan, sauté the mushrooms, onion and celery in the oil until tender. Stir in 2 cups of water and bring to a boil. In a measuring cup, combine the cornstarch and cold water with a fork until smooth and add to the mushroom mixture. Continue to cook and stir the mixture until thickened and bubbly. Add the almonds and the rice to the mushroom mixture and stir well.

Transfer everything to a greased 13 x 9 inch baking dish. Cover and bake at 350° F for 30 minutes.

Uncover and bake for 15 minutes longer or until heated through.

Per serving: 105 calories, 3.7 g protein, 13 g carbohydrates, 4.9 g total fat, 0.5 g saturated fat, 2.1 g fiber, 180 mg sodium, 0.8 g sugar.

Almond-Mushroom Wild Rice

4 servings

1 cup uncooked wild rice
3 cups chicken broth
1 cup sliced fresh mushrooms
½ cup slivered almonds, toasted
2 tbsp. oil
2 tbsp. diced green onions
1 tsp. dried parsley flakes

Rinse and drain the rice. Spoon it into a 9" x 9" baking dish coated with non-stick cooking spray. Add the remaining ingredients. Mix well. Cover and bake at 325° F for 1-½ – 2 hours or until the liquid is absorbed and the rice is tender.

Per serving: 190 calories, 5.8 g protein, 13 g carbohydrates, 14 g total fat, 2.1 g saturated fat, 2.7 g fiber, 720 mg sodium, 1.6 g sugar.

Vegetable Fried Rice

10 servings

6 beaten eggs
2 tbsp. soya sauce
2 tbsp. oil
1 cup minced onions
1 cup minced celery
2 cups minced carrots
2 cups diced mushrooms
2 minced garlic cloves
1 can water chestnuts, drained
1 can baby corn, drained
1 cup snow peas
1 cup bean sprouts
5 cups cold, cooked rice

In a small bowl combine the eggs and 1 tablespoon of the soya sauce. Preheat a large, non-stick frying pan or wok and add 1 tbsp. of oil. When hot, add the egg mixture and cook stirring well. Break up any big egg pieces and set aside.

In the same frying pan or wok, add 1 tbsp. of oil and stir fry the onion, celery, carrots, mushrooms and garlic until crisp tender. Add the cooked rice, the eggs and the remaining ingredients. Cook and stir until heated through. Serve warm.

Per serving: 210 calories, 8 g protein, 31 g carbohydrates, 6 g total fat, 1.4 g saturated fat, 2.6 g fiber, 190 mg sodium, 3 g sugar.

Oven Baked Mushroom Rice

6 servings

1 cup uncooked brown rice
3 tbsp. oil
½ cup diced celery
1 cup diced onions
1 can chicken broth or the equivalent
1 cup water
2 tbsp. soya sauce
1 tbsp. dried parsley flakes
1 cup sliced fresh mushrooms

In a large, non-stick frying pan, sauté the rice in the oil for 2 minutes or until golden brown. Add the celery and onions, then cook and stir for 2 – 3 minutes. Add the mushrooms and continue to cook and stir until bubbling. Transfer to a greased 13 x 11 baking dish. Add the broth, water, soya sauce and parsley flakes.

Cover and bake at 350° F for 60 minutes or until the liquid is absorbed and the rice is tender. Let stand 10 minutes before serving.

Per serving: 120 calories, 19 g protein, 11 g carbohydrates, 7.2 g total fat, 1.1 g saturated fat, 1.4 g fiber, 361 mg sodium, 1 g sugar.

Dirty Rice

4 servings

4 cups water
1 bouillon cube
2 cups white or brown uncooked rice
1 cup diced onions
3 cloves garlic, pressed

In a large saucepan, heat the water and bouillon on high.

In a large, non-stick frying pan, over medium-high heat, cook the oil, onion, garlic and uncooked rice until the rice is browned and sizzling. Stir often.

Add the browned rice mixture into the saucepan with the bouillon and water and cover with a lid. Let heat until the rice mixture boils, and then turn the heat to low for 20 minutes. Let stand for 5 minutes and fluff with a fork.

Per serving: 130 calories, 3 g protein, 27 g carbohydrates, 1 g total fat, 0.2 g saturated fat, 2.5 g fiber, 234 mg sodium, 0.3 g sugar.

PASTA

Stir-Fried Pasta

This recipe is great for left over pasta. My family loves it!

Leftover pasta (If your pasta is stuck together, place it on a cutting board and cut it into bite-sized pieces)

1 cup diced onions
2 cloves of minced garlic
¼ cup oil

Preheat a frying pan on medium-high and coat the pan with oil. Fry up your onions and garlic until tender and add the pasta. Keep stirring until bubbling and browned around the edges.

Shrimp Pasta Primavera

5 servings

6 cups cooked angel hair pasta
2 cups green beans, diced
1 cup sliced fresh mushrooms
½ cup diced onions
2 minced garlic cloves
¼ cup oil
10 jumbo shrimp, peeled and deveined
1 cup chicken broth
¼ tsp. sea salt
1 tbsp. minced fresh basil
1 tbsp. dried oregano leaves
1 tbsp. dried parsley flakes

Cook the pasta according to package directions.

In a large, non-stick frying pan, sauté the green beans, mushrooms, onions and garlic in the oil for 5 minutes. Add the shrimp, broth, sea salt and spices.

Simmer uncovered for 5 minutes or until the shrimp turn pink.

Serve over hot pasta.

Per serving: 400 calories, 14 g protein, 43 g carbohydrates, 13 g total fat, 2 g saturated fat, 5 g fiber, 252 mg sodium, 1.4 g sugar.

Shrimp Fettuccine

8 servings

6 cups cooked fettuccine
2 lbs. uncooked medium shrimp, peeled and deveined
2 minced garlic cloves
¼ cup oil
¼ cup chopped fresh cilantro
2 tbsp. lemon juice
1 cup chicken broth
½ tsp. sea salt
Dash black pepper

Cook the fettuccine noodles according to package directions.

In a large, non-stick frying pan, sauté the shrimp in the garlic and oil for 4 minutes or until the shrimp turn pink. Add the cilantro, lemon juice, broth, sea salt and pepper. Cook and stir for 2 minutes or until the mixture is bubbling.

Serve over hot pasta.

Per serving: 333 calories, 30 g protein, 32 g carbohydrates, 8.8 g total fat, 1.3 g saturated fat, 1.5 g fiber, 395 mg sodium, 3 g sugar.

Marinated Shrimp Pasta

6 servings

2 lbs. uncooked large shrimp, peeled and deveined
2 tbsp. oil
3 diced green onions
2 tbsp. fresh lime juice
2 tbsp. balsamic vinegar
3 tbsp. oil
2 tsp. Dijon mustard
¼ cup liquid honey
1 garlic clove, minced
Hot, cooked pasta

In a non-stick frying pan, over medium-high heat, grill or cook the shrimp for 2-3 minutes on each side or until the shrimp turn pink. Mix the remaining ingredients and pour into a resealable freezer bag, then add the shrimp. Refrigerate for at least 2 hours.

30 minutes before you want to eat, heat a non-stick frying pan, and add the shrimp mixture and marinating sauce. Cook until hot and bubbling, stirring often. Toss with your hot, freshly made pasta and serve.

Per serving: 270 calories, 30 g protein, 14 g carbohydrates, 9.4 g total fat, 1.4 g saturated fat, 0.3 g fiber, 286 mg sodium, 12 g sugar.

Seafood Linguini

8 servings

6 cups cooked linguini
3 cups sliced fresh mushrooms
1 cup diced onions
2 minced garlic cloves
¼ cup oil
2 cups crabmeat, cartilage removed
2 cups shrimp
1 cup green beans, diced
1 cup white wine
1 tsp. dried basil
1 tsp. oregano leaves
½ tsp. sea salt
2 tbsp. butter
2 tbsp. flour
2 cups chicken broth
1 cup frozen peas

Cook the linguini according to package directions.

In a large saucepan, sauté the mushrooms, onions, and garlic in the oil over medium-high heat until golden brown. Add all of the seafood, the green beans, wine and spices and bring to a boil.

In a medium-sized saucepan, melt the butter, add the flour and stir into a paste. Add the chicken broth and mix well. Continue to stir and cook until the sauce thickens. Then pour over the seafood mixture, add the frozen peas and cook 5 more minutes until hot and bubbling.

Serve over hot pasta.

Per serving: 395 calories, 28 g protein, 41 g carbohydrates, 12 g total fat, 3.4 g saturated fat, 3.9 g fiber, 545 mg sodium, 2.3 g sugar.

Linguini with Clam Sauce

6 servings

6 cups cooked linguini
½ cup minced onions
2 minced garlic cloves
½ cup chopped fresh basil
3 tbsp. oil
2 large cans clams with juice
1 cup white wine
1 tsp. parsley flakes
1 tsp. oregano flakes
½ tsp. sea salt

Cook the pasta according to package directions.

In a large saucepan, sauté the onions, garlic and fresh basil in the oil until tender. Add the rest of the ingredients and cook over medium-high heat until bubbling. Reduce the heat and simmer for 5 minutes.

Serve over hot pasta.

Per serving: 223 calories, 16 g protein, 18 g carbohydrates, 8.1 g total fat, 0.9 g saturated fat, 1.0 g fiber, 255 mg sodium, 0.3 g sugar.

Thai Shrimp Stir-Fry

8 servings

6 cups cooked fettuccini or linguini noodles
1 cup snow peas
½ cup diced green onions
1 cup shredded carrots
1 cup diced celery
2 tsp. oil
1 cup chicken broth
1 tsp. corn starch
2 tbsp. soya sauce
1 tbsp. white or red wine vinegar
2 tsp. liquid honey
½ tsp. ginger
2 minced garlic cloves
1 lb. cooked shrimp (thaw if frozen)

Cook the pasta according to the package directions.

In a large, non-stick frying pan or wok, over medium-high heat, cook the vegetables in the oil until crisp-tender, stirring often.

In a large measuring cup, mix the chicken broth, corn starch, soya sauce, vinegar, liquid honey, ginger and garlic. Stir until smooth. Add to the vegetable mixture and cook for 5 more minutes until the sauce is bubbly and slightly thickened. Stir in the shrimp and cook until just heated through, approximately 3-5 minutes. Do not overcook or the shrimp will become rubbery.

Serve over hot pasta.

Per serving: 250 calories, 18 g protein, 39 g carbohydrates, 3.0 g total fat, 0.4 g saturated fat, 2.7 g fiber, 371 mg sodium, 4.7 g sugar.

VEGGIES

Barbequed Vegetables

8 servings

4-5 large potatoes, peeled and cubed
6-8 carrots, peeled and diced
2 cups diced onions
¼ cup oil
2 minced garlic cloves
Parsley flakes
1 tsp. sea salt
1 tsp. black pepper

Lay out two large pieces of aluminum foil with the shiny side facing up on your counter. Pile half of the vegetables on each piece of foil. Drizzle 2 tbsp. of oil over each pile of vegetables. Sprinkle the garlic, parsley flakes, sea salt and pepper over top. Wrap up each piece of foil, tucking in ends firmly.

Wrap each vegetable package once more with another big piece of aluminum foil, dull side out. Place the foil packages on the top rack of the BBQ over medium-low heat for at least an hour.

Open one package carefully to test for doneness.

Please note: You can cook vegetables like this in your oven instead of on your BBQ. Place the vegetables in a large roasting pan. Add the oil and the spices over top and mix well. Cover the pan with aluminum foil, dull side out. Bake at 350° F for an hour or until the vegetables are cooked through.

Per serving: 222 calories, 4.3 g protein, 37 g carbohydrates, 7.2 g total fat, 1.0 g saturated fat, 6.3 g fiber, 380 mg sodium, 6.4 g sugar.

Dairy-Free Mashed Potatoes

Use chicken broth instead of milk, butter or margarine to make your mashed potatoes fluffy. They will taste great and have the benefit of no dairy and less fat.

Carrots in Almond Sauce

5 servings

10 carrots, julienned
½ cup thinly sliced green onions
3 tbsp. oil
1 tsp. cornstarch
½ cup water
1 tsp. chicken bouillon granules
½ tsp. dill weed
½ cup sliced almonds, toasted

In a saucepan, cook the carrots in a small amount of water until crisp-tender, then drain. Transfer to a serving bowl and keep warm. In the same pan, sauté the green onions in the oil for 2 minutes.

In a large measuring cup, combine the cornstarch and water until smooth. Stir into the onion mixture. Add the bouillon granules, dill and almonds. Bring to a boil over medium heat; cook and stir for 5 minutes or until thickened and bubbly. Pour over top of the carrots and garnish with a pinch of dill.

Per serving: 234 calories, 4.5 g protein, 26 g carbohydrates, 14 g total fat, 1.5 g saturated fat, 7.4 g fiber, 325 mg sodium, 10 g sugar.

Stir-Fried Veggies

6 servings

2 cups sliced mushrooms
4 celery stalks thinly sliced on the diagonal
3 peeled carrots, thinly sliced on the diagonal
2 diced green onions
2 cups snow peas, washed
1 small zucchini washed and sliced thin
1 can sliced water chestnuts
1 cup chicken broth
1 clove minced garlic
½ tsp. ginger
3 tsp. soya sauce
2 cups bean sprouts
¼ cup sesame seeds

Preheat a wok or large, non-stick frying pan on high, then add the vegetables (except the bean sprouts) and broth. Cook and stir for 10 minutes. In a measuring cup, mix the garlic, ginger and soya sauce, and pour over the vegetables. Stir fry for an additional 5 minutes. Add the bean sprouts and sesame seeds and toss well before serving.

Per serving: 120 calories, 5.5 g protein, 20 g carbohydrates, 3.5 g total fat, 0.6 g saturated fat, 6.4 g fiber, 344 mg sodium, 7.4 g sugar.

Baked Winter Vegetables

12 servings

8 cups sweet potatoes, peeled and diced
8 cups potatoes, peeled and diced
8 cups diced carrots
1 celery root, peeled and diced (these look like brown fuzzy turnips)
½ cup packed brown sugar
4 minced garlic cloves
¼ cup water
¼ cup oil
1 tsp. salt
2 cups chicken broth

In a large bowl, mix the all of the vegetables. In a large measuring cup, combine the remaining ingredients and drizzle them over the vegetables. Mix well and spread evenly in two large baking pans. Cover with aluminum foil (dull side out) and bake at 400° F for 30-40 minutes.

Stir vegetables and bake uncovered for another 30 minutes until the vegetables are browned at the edges and tender inside.

Per serving: 275 calories, 4.8 g protein, 58 g carbohydrates, 4.8 g total fat, 0.7 g saturated fat, 7.3 g fiber, 92mg sodium, 24 g sugar.

Pickled Green Beans

4 servings

4 whole garlic cloves
2 lb. fresh green beans, trimmed
1 tsp. dill
½ cup water
½ cup vinegar
1 tsp. salt

Fill a large saucepan with water and bring to a boil. Add the beans and cook for 3 minutes, then drain, rinse with cold water and drain again.

In a large pickle jar, pack the beans so that they stand upright, then add the garlic cloves, dill, water, vinegar and salt. If there is not enough liquid to cover the beans, add equal amounts of vinegar and water until covered. Screw the lid on tightly and shake well. Let sit in your refrigerator for at least one day before eating.

Per serving: 40 calories, 2.1 g protein, 10 g carbohydrates, 0.1 g total fat, 0 g saturated fat, 3.8 g fiber, 588 mg sodium, 1.8 g sugar.

Oven Roasted Green Beans

These are a healthy alternative to French fries.

6 servings

2 lbs. green beans
¼ cup oil
2 minced garlic cloves
Salt and pepper to taste

Preheat your oven to 450°F convection bake. (YES! 450°F)

Wash and clip the ends off the green beans. Place them in a large bowl. Drizzle the oil over top. Crush the garlic with a garlic press and add to the mix and toss again.

Place parchment paper on three cookie sheets and spread the beans evenly over all three. Sprinkle salt and pepper over top of the beans and place in your oven.

Roast for about 5 minutes, then stir and let roast another 5. Check often to make sure that your beans don't burn. They should be browned and sizzling when done.

Per serving: 60 calories, 3.4 g protein, 13 g carbohydrates, 0.2 g total fat, 0 g saturated fat, 6.3 g fiber, 398 mg sodium, 0 g sugar.

Sweet Potato Fries

8 servings

2 lb. sweet potatoes
¼ cup oil
1 tsp. garlic powder
1 tsp. onion powder
1 tsp. salt
1 tsp. pepper

Peel and cut the sweet potatoes into long narrow strips (like french fries) and place into a large mixing bowl. In a large measuring cup, combine the oil and spices and beat well. Pour over the potatoes and toss to coat.

Place the potato strips in a single layer on two baking sheets lined with parchment paper. Bake, uncovered, at 450°F convection bake for 15 minutes, turn and bake for another 15 minutes or until golden brown.

Per serving: 162 calories, 1 g protein, 10 g carbohydrates, 13.6 g total fat, 1.8 g saturated fat, 1.5 g fiber, 600 mg sodium, 3.8 g sugar.

Potato Salad

10 servings

8 cups red potatoes, scrubbed and diced
2 cups diced carrots
1 cup diced celery
2 tsp. dried parsley flakes
¼ cup red wine vinegar
1 tbsp. oil
1 tsp. liquid honey
1 tsp. Dijon mustard
1 minced garlic clove
Dash pepper

Steam the potatoes for 10 minutes, then add the carrots and continue to steam for another 10 minutes or until cooked through. Drain off any excess water. In a large bowl, toss the potatoes, carrots, celery and parsley flakes until well mixed. In a measuring cup, whisk together the vinegar, oil, liquid honey, Dijon mustard, garlic and pepper. Pour over the potato mixture and stir gently until evenly coated with dressing. Serve warm or cold.

Per serving: 115 calories, 2.4 g protein, 24 g carbohydrates, 1.5 g total fat, 0.2 g saturated fat, 3.8 g fiber, 60 mg sodium, 4.3 g sugar.

Corn and Avocado Salad

8 servings

4 cups frozen corn, soaked in warm water and drained
2 avocados, peeled and diced
1 cup toasted sunflower seeds
1 cup diced celery
1 cup shredded carrots
¼ cup toasted almonds
3 tbsp. oil
1 tsp. Dijon Mustard
¼ cup white wine vinegar
2 tbsp. liquid honey

In a large mixing bowl, add the corn, avocado, sunflower seeds, celery, carrots and almonds. In a measuring cup, mix the oil with the mustard and stir until smooth (this can take a minute or so). Add the vinegar and the liquid honey. If you find the dressing too "vinegary", add more honey to taste. Pour the dressing over top of the vegetables and mix well.

Per serving: 395 calories, 9.8 g protein, 37 g carbohydrates, 27 g total fat, 3.1 g saturated fat, 9.4 g fiber, 47 mg sodium, 9.6 g sugar.

Roasted Potato Salad

10 servings

4 cups water
3 cups fresh green beans, diced
2 lbs. small red potatoes, quartered
5 cups diced carrots
2 diced green onions
3 minced garlic cloves
1 cup chicken broth
3 tbsp. balsamic vinegar
2 tbsp. oil
2 tsp. liquid honey
¼ tsp. dried crushed rosemary
¼ tsp. oregano leaves
1 tsp. sea salt

In a large saucepan, bring the water to a boil. Add the green beans, cover and cook for 3 minutes. Drain and immediately pour cold water over the beans. Let sit until cool. Drain with a colander and keep until needed.

In a large, greased baking pan, add the potatoes, carrots, green onions, and garlic. Pour the broth over top and bake, uncovered at 400° F for one hour or until vegetables are cooked through. When done, remove from the oven and stir in the beans.

In a measuring cup, mix the vinegar, oil, liquid honey and spices. Pour over top of the vegetables and mix well.

Serve warm or cold.

Per serving: 180 calories, 4 g protein, 36 g carbohydrates, 3.0 g total fat, 0.5 g saturated fat, 6.7 g fiber, 400 mg sodium, 6.5 g sugar.

Baked Sweet Potatoes

4 servings

4 medium sweet potatoes peeled and sliced into ¼ inch thick rounds
1 cup unsweetened apple juice
1 tsp. ginger
1 tbsp. brown sugar

Preheat your oven to 425° F. Combine all ingredients in a large bowl and mix well. Spread the mixture evenly in a greased medium casserole dish. Bake uncovered for 60 minutes until the potatoes are golden brown and most of the liquid is evaporated.

Serve warm.

Per serving: 145 calories, 2.4 g protein, 35 g carbohydrates, 0.2 g total fat, 0.1 g saturated fat, 3.9 g fiber, 45 mg sodium, 20 g sugar.

Baked Potato Wedges

4 servings

4 large potatoes, unpeeled, scrubbed
1 tbsp. oil
Dried parsley flakes
Sea Salt
Dash pepper

Preheat your oven to 400° F. Cut each potato lengthwise into 4 quarters. Then cut each quarter into wedges. Place the potato wedges in a large bowl and add the oil and spices. Toss well.

Transfer the potatoes to 2 large baking sheets that have been lined with parchment paper. Spread the potatoes evenly and bake for 30 minutes. Turn the wedges over and bake another 20 minutes, until the potatoes are golden brown on the outside and tender on the inside.

Per serving: 133 calories, 2.5 g protein, 24 g carbohydrates, 3.4 g total fat, 0.5 g saturated fat, 3.6 g fiber, 605 mg sodium, 1.7 g sugar.

Garlic Mushrooms

5 servings

5 cups fresh mushrooms
3 tbsp. oil
2 minced garlic cloves
1 diced green onion
½ cup white wine
½ tsp. sea salt

Preheat a large, non-stick frying pan to medium-high. Add the mushrooms and oil and stir for 5-10 minutes. When nicely browned, add the garlic, green onion, white wine and salt. Continue to cook for another 5 minutes.

Serve over steak or chicken, or spoon over a baked potato.

Per serving: 105 calories, 2.3 g protein, 3 g carbohydrates, 8.3 g total fat, 1.1 g saturated fat, 1.0 g fiber, 35 mg sodium, 1.3 g sugar.

Acorn Squash Casserole

This recipe is loved by all who try it!

12 servings

4 acorn squash
¼ cup margarine
3 eggs, beaten
1 tsp salt – this is necessary!

Topping

1 cup margarine
2 cups brown sugar
1 cup flour
2 cups pecans

Cut the acorn squash in half and place face down on a greased cookie sheet. Add ½ cup water to the cookie sheet and bake uncovered at 350° for approximately one hour. Test your squash by sticking a fork into it. It should be soft and easy to mash with your fork. Let cool. Scoop the flesh of the squash into a bowl and mash with the margarine, eggs and salt. Pat into a greased casserole dish.

To make the topping, melt the margarine in a saucepan. Add the brown sugar, flour and pecans and mix until smooth. Drop in spoonfuls over the squash mixture.

Bake at 350° for approximately 30 minutes. The topping should be browned and the squash mixture bubbling.

Per serving: 475 calories, 5.6 g protein, 50 g carbohydrates, 34 g total fat, 14 g saturated fat, 4.2 g fiber, 360 mg sodium, 26 g sugar.

Homemade Bread and Butter Pickles

Pickles

30-50 baby cucumbers
1 medium onion

Brine

4 cups sugar
¼ cup salt
1½ tsp. turmeric
4 cups vinegar
1½ tsp. mustard seed

Slice baby cucumbers thinly to fill ¾ of an ice cream pail

Cut the onion into quarters and then slice as finely as possible and add to the pail.

Pour the brine ingredients into a medium-sized saucepan. Bring to a boil, then let cool completely. Pour over the cucumbers and onions. Cover the ice cream pail with the lid and let stand in your fridge for 5 days.

Will keep for 8 months in your fridge!

Notes

References

[1] Hill DJ, Hudson IL, et al. A low allergen diet is a significant intervention in infantile colic: results of a community-based study. J Allergy Clin Immunol 1995; 96(6): 886-92.

[2] Lee C, Cheng TL. Bonding. Pediatr Rev 2003; 24(8): 289-90.

[3] Fergusson DM, Woodward LJ. Breastfeeding and later psychosocial adjustment. Paediatr Perinat Epidemiol 1999; 13(2): 144-57.

[4] Hormann E. Breastfeeding your older baby. Mothering 1993; winter: 84-88.

[5] Lawrence, Ruth A.; Lawrence, Robert M. Breastfeeding: A Guide for the Medical Professional (pp. 274-275). Elsevier Health Sciences. Kindle Edition.

[6] www.icpa4kids.org

[7] Colin N. Congenital muscular torticollis: a review, case study and proposed protocol for chiropractic management. Top Clin Chiro 1998; 5(3): 27-33.

[8] Carenzio G, Carlisi E, Morani I, et al. Early Rehabilitation treatment in newborns with congenital muscular torticollis. Eur J Phys Rehabil Med 2015 Oct; 51(5): 539-45.

[9] Kuo AA, Tritasavit S, Graham JM Jr. Congenital muscular torticollis and positional plagiocephaly. Pediatr Rev 2014 Feb; 35(2): 79-87.

[10] Seo SJ, Yim SY, Lee IJ, et al. Is craniofacial asymmetry progressive in untreated congenital muscular torticollis? Plast Reconstr Surg 2013 Aug; 132(2): 407-13.

[11] Genna CW. Breastfeeding infants with congenital torticollis. J Hum Lact 2015 May; 31(2): 216-20.

[12] Cheng JC, Tang SP, et al. The clinical presentation and outcome of treatment of congenital muscular torticollis in infants—a study of 1,086 cases. J Pediatr Surg 2000; 35(7): 1091-6.

[13] Cheng JC, Wong MW, et al. Clinical determinants of the outcome of manual stretching in the treatment of congenital muscular torticollis in infants. A prospective study of eight hundred and twenty-one cases. J Bone Joint Surg Am 2001; 83A(5): 679-87.

[14] Toto BJ. Chiropractic correction of congenital muscular torticollis. J Manip Physiol Ther 1993; 16(8): 556-9.

[15] Fallon JM, Fysh PN. Chiropractic care of the newborn with congenital torticollis. J Clin Chiro Peds 1997; 2(1): 113-5.

[16] http://www.mayoclinic.org/diseases-conditions/tongue-tie/basics/definition/con-20035410

[17] Coryllos, E. Watson Genna, C. Salloum, A. (2004), Congenital tongue-tie and its impact on breastfeeding American Academy of Pediatrics Section on Breastfeeding Newsletter, Summer 2004; 3.

[18] Anrig CA, Plaugher G. Pediatric Chiropractic. Lippincott, Williams & Wilkins. Philadelphia: 2013; 769.

[19] Marko, S. The Effect of Chiropractic Care on an Infant with Problems of Constipation: A Case Study. Chiropractic Pediatrics Vol. 1 No. 3 Dec. 1994.

[20] Batte S. Resolution of colic, constipation and sleep disturbance in an infant following chiropractic care to reduce vertebral subluxation [case report]. J Pediatr Matern & Fam Health – Chiropr: Win 2010 (2010:1: Online access only) 1-5.

[21] Ressel O, Rudy R. Vertebral subluxation correlated with somatic, visceral and immune complaints: an analysis of 650 children under chiropractic care. J Vert Sublux Res: 2004 (Oct:18: Online access only) 23

[22] Alcantara J, Mayer DM. The successful chiropractic care of pediatric patients with chronic constipation: A case series and selective review of the literature [case report, review]. Clin Chiropr: Sep 2008 (11:3) 138-147.

[23] A great explanation of how the nerves supply the bowel and anus can be found at www.spinalhub.com.au/what-is-a-spinal-cord-injury/your-bowel-and-spinal-cord-injury/nervous-system-control-of-your-bowel

[24] Lawrence, R. Human milk as a prophylaxis in allergy. In: Breastfeeding. A guide for the medical profession. St. Louis: Mosby publishers, 1994, 541-553.

[25] Sampson HA, Anderson JA. Summary and recommendations: classification of gastrointestinal manifestations due to immunologic reactions to foods in infants and young children. J Pediatr Gastroenterol Nutr 2000; 30(Suppl): S87-94.

[26] www.aaaai.org/conditions-and-treatments/allergies

[27] Vandenplas Y, Loeb H. Extra-digestive manifestations of food allergy. Arch Pediatr 1994; 1(1): 57-60.

[28] Riordan J, Auerbach K. Breastfeeding and human lactation. Boston: Jones and Bartlett publishers, 1999: 657.

[29] Renz H et al. Breastfeeding modifies production of sIgA cow's milk-antibodies in infants. Acta Paediatr Scand 1991; 80: 149-154.

[30] Ewing WM, Allen PJ. The diagnosis and management of cow milk protein intolerance in the primary care setting. Pediatr Nurs 2005 Nov-Dec; 31(6): 486-93.

[31] Sampson HA, Anderson JA. Summary and recommendations: classification of gastrointestinal manifestations due to immunologic reactions to foods in

infants and young children. J Pediatr Gastroenterol Nutr 2000; 30(Suppl): S87-94.

[32] Ahmed T, Fuchs GJ. Gastrointestinal allergy to food: a review. J Diarrhoeal Dis Res. 1997 Dec; 15(4): 211-23

[33] Lifschitz C, Szajewska H. Cow's milk allergy: evidence-based diagnosis and management for the practitioner. Eur J Pediatr 2015 Feb; 174(2): 141-50.

[34] Host A. Frequency of cow's milk allergy in childhood. Ann Allergy Asthma Immunol. 2002 Dec; 89(6 Suppl 1): 33-7.

[35] Miceli Sopo S, Monaco S, Greco M, Scala G. Chronic food protein-induced enterocolitis syndrome caused by cow's milk proteins passed through breast milk. Int Arch Allergy Immunol 2014; 164(3): 207-9.

[36] Lindberg T. Infantile colic and small intestinal function: a nutritional problem? Acta Paediatr Suppl. 1999; 8(430): 58-60.

[37] Clyne PS, Kulczycki A Jr. Human breastmilk contains bovine IgG. Relationship to infant colic? Pediatrics 1991; 87(4): 439-44.

[38] Jarvinen KM, Makinen-Kiljunen S, Suomalainen H. Cow's milk challenge through human milk evokes immune responses in infants with cow's milk allergy. J Pediatr 1999; 135(4): 506-12.

[39] Jakobsson I, Lindberg T. Cow's milk proteins cause infantile colic in breastfed infants: a double-blind crossover study. Pediatrics 1983; 71(2): 268-71.

[40] Lothe L, Lindberg T, Jakobsson I. Macromolecular absorption in infants with infantile colic. Acta Paediatr Scand 1990; 79(4): 417-21.

[41] Jakobsson I., Lindberg T. Cow's milk proteins cause infantile colic in breast-fed infants: a double-blind crossover study. Pediatrics. 1983;71:268.

[42] Lothe L, Lindberg T. Cow's milk whey protein elicits symptoms of infantile colic in colicky formula-fed infants: a double-blind crossover study. Pediatrics 1989; 83(2): 262-6.

[43] Iacono G, Carroccio A et al. Severe infantile colic and food intolerance: a long term prospective study. J Pediatr Gastroenterol Nutr 1991; 12(3): 332-5.

[44] Lothe L, Lindberg T, Jakobsson I. Macromolecular absorption in infants with infantile colic. Acta Paediatr Scand 1990; 79(4): 417-21.

[45] Cooper RL, Cooper MN. Red pepper-induced dermatitis in breast-fed infants. Dermatology. 1996; 193: 61.

[46] Lust KD, Brown JE, Thomas W. Maternal intake of cruciferous vegetables and other foods and colic symptoms in exclusively breastfed infants. J Am Diet Assoc. 1996; 96(1): 46-8.

[47] Lawrence RA, Lawrence R. Breastfeeding. A guide for the medical profession. Philadelphia: Elsevier Publishers, 2016: 315.

[48] Lust KD, Brown JE, Thomas W. Maternal intake of cruciferous vegetables and other foods and colic symptoms in exclusively breastfed infants. J Am Diet Assoc. 1996; 96(1): 46-8.

[49] Haftel L. Berkovich Z, Reifen R. Elevated milk B-Carotene and lycopene after carrot and tomato paste supplementation. Nutrition 2015 Mar; 31(3): 443-5.

[50] Domino EF, Hornbach E, Demana T. The nicotine content of common vegetables. N Engl J Med. 1993; 329: 437.

[51] Metcalfe JR, Marsh JA, et al. Effects of maternal dietary egg intake during early lactation on human milk ovalbumin concentration: a randomized controlled trial. Clin Exp Allergy 2016 Dec; 46(12): 1605-1613.

[52] Grimshaw KE, Bryant T, et al. Incidence and risk factors for food hypersensitivity in UK infants: results from a birth cohort study. Clin Transl Allergy 2016 Jan 26; 6: 1.

[53] Du Toit G, Roberts, G, Sayre, PH, et al. Randomized trial of peanut consumption in infants at risk for peanut allergy. NEJM 2015; 372: 803-813.

[54] Iacono G, Carroccio A, Montalto G. Severe infantile colic and food intolerance: a long-term prospective study. J Pediatr Gastroent Nutr 1991; 12: 332-5.

[55] Lust KD, Brown JE, Thomas W. Maternal intake of cruciferous vegetables and other foods and colic symptoms in exclusively breastfed infants. J Am Diet Assoc. 1996; 96(1): 46-8.

[56] Uenishi T, Sugiura H, Tanaka T, Uehara M. Aggravation of atopic dermatitis in breast-fed infants by tree nut-related foods and fermented foods in breast milk. J Dermatol. 2011 Feb; 38(2): 140-5.

[57] Riordan J, Auerbach K. Breastfeeding and human lactation. Boston: Jones and Bartlett Publishers, 1999: 657.

[58] Newman J, Pitman, T. Dr. Jack Newman's Guide to Breastfeeding. Toronto: 2000: 177.

[59] Mouscan G, Kamat D. Cow's milk protein allergy. Clin Pediatr (Phila) 2016 Oct; 55(11): 1054-63.

[60] Lawrence RA, Lawrence R. Breastfeeding. A guide for the medical profession. Philadelphia: Elsevier Publishers, 2016: 315.

[61] Jamison, JR, Davies NJ. Chiropractic management of cow's milk protein intolerance in infants with sleep dysfunction syndrome: a therapeutic trial. J Manip Phyiol Ther 2006; 29(6): 469-74.

[62] Hill DJ, Hudson IL, Sheffield LJ, et al. A low allergen diet is a significant intervention in infantile colic: results of a community based study. J Allergy Clin Immunol. 1995; 96: 886

[63] Iacono G, Carroccio A, Montalto G. Severe infantile colic and food intolerance: a long-term prospective study. J Pediatr Gastroent Nutr 1991; 12: 332-5.

[64] http://acaai.org/allergies/types/food-allergies/types-food-allergy/soy-allergy

[65] http://acaai.org/allergies/types/food-allergies/types-food-allergy/corn-allergy

[66] Lawrence RA, Lawrence R. Breastfeeding. A guide for the medical profession. Philadelphia: Elsevier Publishers, 2016: 276.

[67] Newman J, Pitman, T. Dr. Jack Newman's guide to Breastfeeding. Toronto: 2000: 177.

[68] http://farrp.unl.edu/resources/gi-fas/opinion-and-summaries/dairy-free-and-non-dairy

[69] Lawrence RA, Lawrence R. Breastfeeding. A guide for the medical profession. Philadelphia: Elsevier Publishers, 2016:276.

[70] Schaal B, et al. Olfactory stimulation in the relationship between child and mother. Reprod Nutr Dev 1980; 20(3B): 843-58.

CPSIA information can be obtained
at www.ICGtesting.com
Printed in the USA
LVHW011928140821
695338LV00010B/567

9 780973 945546